WHAT I
ARE S

Defrocking this Lady provides a rich social history embedded within an epic family narrative against a background of political, social and religious intrigue. An appreciative acknowledgement of the complexity of a family genesis unfolding over time and through generations.

It is an erudite composition by a writer that reflects a lifetime and love of the eclectic written word. He serves up a literary diet rich in consequences in which subject and object often compete for significance within sentences that brim over with meaning. The story employs ornate language and sentence structures that often mimic and evoke an ambiance for their own particular era. The often complex and layered sentences are compacted and qualified in drawing forth complex portraits.

The work is contemplative and self-conscious, reflecting as much about Carlos' journey as that of The Portuguese Lady by embarking on a stream of consciousness, sometimes self-directed. It deploys sophisticated references to specific musical pieces, which coupled with poetry captures a vivid sense of place and feeling.

—Max Dumais, public intellectual.

As a native of South America who lived in Colombia and Argentina and embraced many of the cultures of the continent from Brazil to Chile and Peru, The Portuguese Lady's Earrings is an art piece that most would enjoy but only a few would discuss.

The book offers a window to a wealth of historical richness that has transported me as a reader to live vividly every detail of an era with powerful changes that shaped the world we live in today. It is a privilege to learn history from an impressive and fine researcher, writer and intellectual.

—Luis Romero.

This is a grand sweeping book that slowly reveals the tangled history of the de Oliveira Evora family. At its heart is a story of a mother and son's life - wrapped in mystery for so many years. The themes of dispossession, exile and tragedy run deep but Olga Sara's son Carlos ultimately both learns and remembers the past. In so doing he is mot condemned to repeat it unlike the generations who lived before him. This book, a beautiful reflection on his mother's life and history is assurance she has not lived in vain.

Selochan weaves together the story of the Portuguese empire and its colonial exploits with the intimate story of mother and son coming to terms with who they are and the global forces that have determined their individual fates. There is a wealth of fascinating historical material covered in his narrative. His writing brings alive scenes from domestic life in the wealthy Brazilian household ruled by the patriarch Dom Pedro – sometimes charming, often dark. The book evokes a strong sense of place as Carlos moves around the world – Brazil, England, Europe, the US and Australia - living a life of accomplishments despite his troubled beginnings.

—Virginia Hart.

An extremely powerful story of The Portuguese Lady. A celebration of life and role model to follow. Well-written. Amazing work to memorise and souvenirs. Thanks for sharing!

—Sineth Sar. Cambodian-French Business & Social enterprise entrepreneur.

The author tells haunting stories that shed light on history hidden in nooks and crannies of time. I was captured by heartfelt intrigue and often find myself thinking of this book. It should be read by all generations coming from a Gen Z.

—Renee Cheah.

This book has much reflective thoughts about the lives of the de Oliveira Evora family in different places. At the very start, the story brings the reader to be in the present with Carlos, then witnessing the colourful and emotional past of generations through players and finally returning to the present with one's own self reflections and awe. The facts based narrative of places spin the magic of storytelling that weaves vivid imaginations into one's mind, making the story ideal for film and virtual reality storyboarding. It is a book that once one starts reading, one must finish in the same day. Awesome and thought- provoking reading! Light a candle when you read this book. You will be guided by your own magic that will help you find your own meaning of life.

—Dr Chan Cheah. Futurist & Information and Communication Technology Specialist.

Born in Brazil, this incredibly candid and well researched recount of a family torn apart and the curiosity of one member, to learn of his origins by reconnecting with his mother after a decade leads him to unearth the brutal history and influence of Portugal, its power, greed and exploitation of slavery and the shaping of what Brazil is today.

With each page, I felt present witnessing each moment, event and heartfelt emotions as Carlos looks into the influences on his life.

Captivating to the last page…

—Bruno D'amico.

THE PORTUGUESE LADY'S EARRINGS

A catalogue record for this
work is available from the
National Library of Australia

Viberto Selochan (author)
The Portuguese Lady's Earrings
978-1-922527-8-06

Typeset Minion Pro 11/15

Cover artwork by Livia Ce
Cover and book design by Green Hill Publishing

Although based on real people and real events, the author
does not intend for the book to be read as a literal account.

THE PORTUGUESE LADY'S EARRINGS

VIBERTO SELOCHAN

CONTENTS

A time to sow and a time to reap
A time to tear down and time to build
A time to search and a time to give up
A time to tear and a time to mend
A time to be silent and a time to speak

THE BOOK OF ECCLESIASTES 3:7

Homage to my Mother

Let me not seem to live in vain

PROLOGUE

You will know the truth and the truth will make you free.
JOHN 8:32

On the cusp of the waking dawn, Wednesday the fourteenth of November two thousand and seven was an ordinary day in Tampa bay. Perhaps, for joggers, retirees slowly strolling, and beachcombers meandering, all intent with purpose, witnesses to rushing waves washing away their footprints. Unintentionally, as dawn woke, that shaft of light streaming through the clouds seemed reluctant to herald the autumn day. Portending it would be no ordinary day for the soul of the de Oliveira Evora family. It was the day the Portuguese lady passed away knowingly ending centuries of a federation of ancestors who developed a dynasty with an Empire and died like it, testimony to contradictions.

It was only when that cool autumn wind swirled around him on that Florida morning and he turned to pull the sweater over his shoulder he saw the Portuguese embroidered lace curtain flapped as the sea breeze blew through the window that he knew time and place had died. His tears were mired believing Philosopher George Santayana's dictum: 'Those who cannot remember the past are condemned to repeat it.'

Carlos de Oliveira Evora's footprints washed away too, unobserved, as he wept with thoughts of his mother's life knowing that 'we are all transient, and unsuspectingly swept into the sea of life to disappear like footprints in the sand of time.' Carlos recalled he had forever been contemplating his life, as he always believed that if you do not know where you came from how will you know where you are going?

Reflecting on their penultimate conversation, when the windows were closed and with few distractions, they were looking at each other in the realisation that centuries were closing in on them. His mother, tearful and sad of eyes, firmly said: 'It is only by knowing the past you will understand the present and can plan the future. With my passing, your preconceived notions will be challenged.' Now, that was quintessentially Olga Sara, small of stature, big of heart, equipped with an unforgiving intellect and vivid imagination, simultaneously questioning, and challenging: a skein of contradictions.

On occasions, she would say, 'I do not like to think of problems in the absence of solutions.' There were not many such occasions for Carlos to witness. This was an extraordinarily significant occasion. For decades, mother and son led separate lives, from when he was seven and she was twenty-four. For them, much of their history was still unfolding and to be told.

Carlos had a notion that history is not written by victors but survivors. She challenged that perspective. Olga Sara was one of those whose history was clearly unknown to her and everyone else. Her defining characteristic was that 'life must be based on the need-to-know-principle.' She did not believe that history was just about names and dates, but a narrative. 'The past,' she said, 'will not reveal itself, it must be discussed, interpreted and deconstructed, because people see the past differently, and countries do too. So, recognise and accept that there are alternative points of view which you may not accept but must respect.'

Although Olga Sara advocated that there are times when it is necessary to put aside the past so that you can live with yourself, she believed devaluing the past can lead to confusion. Therefore, it compels you to fashion an identity. Peering through the past was destined to capture her, Carlos believed. Olga Sara also knew that he must do the same to understand the circumstances that determined their lives.

Carlos lived with the notion that like his identity, his destiny was undetermined. Inventing an identity was unnecessary when you can unravel it to find the truth, but he still had to. From Sao Paulo, Brazil, reputedly the son of Joseph dos Barros, but with certainty of Olga Sara de Oliveira Evora. He was educated by Jesuits until he was seven years old. Of them, Father Bridges, an Englishman and Father Morrison, an Irishman, were influential in determining the course of his life. They taught him all experiences are character building.

Growing up Carlos believed his identity was formed by the dominant people in his life. At school, identity was predominantly shaped by the interaction and the influence of his peers. As a mixed-race child, he experienced an automatic assumption that identified him with the minority race. Stereotyping was a *tour de force* which became a life-long challenge for him. It was indeed because the major influence and exposure were with the dominant race with no exposure to the minority race: Portuguese and Brazilian parentage and English public school.

The Jesuits taught him that people fashion identity when they do not know or like the identity they are assumed to be. In Sao Paulo, the Jesuits imbued him with a passion for knowledge. Initially in England, it was more about struggling to understand and uncover his identity to find his place. There were times when he assumed he had found a place. Yet, he resumed his quest. Deprived, Carlos knew little about himself. Olga Sara had said little or just enough to comfort them both.

Initially, it was surmised from a decade of separate lives with no conversation, it left them with many unanswered questions that needed to be addressed. But it continued that way until circumstances fashioned mutual curiosity. Then as familiarity developed and urgency increased, it gradually became easier for them to share memories of those missing four decades. While apart, urgency did not prevail, until the choice was not for them to determine. When conversation flowed, as they knew it must, they feared it may be too late, wondering whether memories would allow them to uncover the truth about each other's identity.

Carlos arrived in England when he was seven. Olga Sara arrived in Brazil when she was seven. The assumption was that mother and son identified with each other. Stories were theirs to share. Olga Sara asked many times for him to talk about his life at boarding school in Surrey which, as the most wooded county in England, became his sanctuary. Carlos would regularly escape to those woods, covered with bluebells in Spring or with giant oaks shimmering with leaves of gold in autumn.

In the solitude of his loneliness in the woods of Surrey and its rolling Downs where he searched for answers, were stories he never told Olga Sara as for them the time was never right, and circumstances never allowed, even when they were alone together. But then they never met during that lost decade. When they had the opportunity, he was seventeen. For sure, it was not what a teenage boy wanted to discuss with his mother, or so it appears they thought. They were destined to live separate lives.

It took four decades before he was confident and ready to tell her about those missing years. For sure she too was ready and waiting. There were many things she knew he would never know, but now must. Yet she could not tell him of their parting when she struggled in a fugue of anger and sorrow as her opinion was not sought or valued when her seven-year-old son was winged away. All she could offer him was what she had been offered at that age, coming from a family that was historically imbued with dynastic thinking. Preserved by historical silence.

The family tradition was to keep a journal to record your life, as she would say, 'our family did for centuries, so we must continue to record our stories.' Searching many years later, he found that although the dynasty was advocated, planned, and executed by men, women recorded stories of their families. Men only recorded events when they were at sea or in far off lands. Emotional outbursts were scribbled in the margins of their records. Astonishingly, when they corresponded, it was generally interspersed with gossip.

That call came. From Carmelita in Tampa bay, it was approaching mother's final days. In Melbourne, Carlos contemplated that he and Olga Sara must deliver on their promises to each other. Obsessively preparing himself, a trait he inherited from his mother, for the encounter which they had to confront, knowing it was going to be untimely and life changing. A dilemma of his life on this matter was that he could not conceptualise where to begin. They both had disrupted lives, lived in places far away from family and where they were born. Both having no say or choice.

Suddenly, lost in a miasma of despair and with the realisation that he was about to embark on a journey he did not envisage. To a city he did not know from one he knew well, having lived there for over three decades. Carlos sought solace hoping it would help bring clarity. Deep in contemplation, walking from his home at Badgers Wood on Edna Walling Estate, eponymous with the English-born and Australia's most influential twentieth-century garden designer. In the heritage-listed village she built, houses and gardens are in symmetry. Searching in time and places he hoped and prayed would offer answers. Walling's estate is coterminous with Yering Station, one of the oldest wineries in Victoria's Yarra Valley. A place he knew so well he even thought he could find answers as he morbidly and aimlessly wandered the vineyards with buds peering from vines of Shiraz grapes, seemingly eager to burst with the sunlight of a Spring morning in the Southern Hemisphere.

An hour away, Melbourne beckoned. Carlos responded. In St Francis, anchored in meditation, he was seeking serenity in a Catholic church, the oldest in the state, built before the gold rush in Victoria. That church still maintained its ecclesiastical solemnity and imagery, offering space to reflect and contemplate, facilitated by lighting ten candles for the decade when mother and son were lost from each other. Preparing to say goodbye to this Australian city, known for trams, artistic and culinary culture, overlaid with architectural splendour of nineteenth-century buildings, all adding to and contributing to the city's European milieu, in recognition of its early settlers. Coexisting on land with the oldest civilisation in the world, emitting the spirituality of its indigenous people for over sixty thousand years.

Mired in the duality of spirituality accentuated his soul search, Carlos walked past the Town Hall built in 1854 in the Second Empire architectural style, fronted with daffodils and a cornucopia of flowers in full Spring bloom. Nearby stands the Anglican Cathedral of St Pauls nodding in recognition to the iconic Railway Station across Flinders Street. Crossing the Yarra River on the Princes Bridge, Carlos search led to his favourite walk in Alexandra gardens in full splendour in honour of his mother's love of gardens. A tradition handed down for over a hundred years from her female ancestors. Olga Sara's contribution was in her design and development of gardens in the many countries where she lived.

With clarity of purpose, Carlos now believed he was equipped to plan his visit to Tampa. Where better from, he thought. So as of habit, he wandered into Degraves lane. Always inviting, with its clustering of patisseries above which are buildings with overhanging balconies with boxes of plants brimming with a kaleidoscope of colours offsetting handcrafted antique signs. Bookended by the gothic architecture of the Majorca building and the western entrance of Flinders Street railway station.

Comfortably seated there, hovering over a glass of Yering red and a stream of cappuccinos, Carlos lingered in the atmosphere of boisterous carefree groups in rapturous laughter, interspersed with the bellowing of cathedral bells. Intermingling with live music reverberating off graffiti walls of rainbow colours, ever-present in that environment; he was immersed in the odour of many flavours of coffee. Imbibed and imbued, Carlos felt at peace as he farewelled a city he loved for a city with no certainty. For him, it was the tyranny of distance.

Arriving in Tampa, he was surprised by his mother's dignity without expectations. Confronting her resignation, was a woman he always felt was strong and resilient. That is why, he thought on reflection, only a woman of her endurance could portray such a demeanour. It made the carefully constructed and crafted dialogue, Carlos contemplated he would say, superfluous. As was the cadence he practised in which it would be delivered, having designed, and rehearsed it in his Melbourne musings. Inviting him, his mother offered simplicity in delivery. Yet he was to blunder.

Unnoticed and unobserved, but with dignity Olga Sara peacefully waited in urgency. She did not betray it but remained cognisant that time was constrained. Precious to all but especially to a mother and son who had been disconnected, and never seemed able to connect, then, as of now, both desired nothing less than time with each other.

Carlos took a measured approach in his conversation with Olga Sara. Neither knowing nor having expectations of how delicate the stories they had avoided could be, or of its impact on them as they embarked on the journey to exchange unknowable stories. Paramount in his thinking was her need to know principle. As he contemplated Olga Sara's rule for life, he wondered what it was for journey's end.

Standing up from the comfort of her well-worn brown chesterfield armchair, where he always pictured her sitting, book in hand with music of her favourite composers in the background, as she compulsively and obsessively cultivated. In her final hours, she was still captive to habits of a lifetime. It made him reflect on his obsessions and how it may have indelible consequences. But this was not about him. Confronting his obsessiveness, Carlos was compelled to ask, but would Olga Sara be courageous enough to answer? After all, they missed those formative years when these matters would have been a feature of their lives. But now was their time. Blundering, 'Excuse me, mother,' he avers, 'you never explained to my satis-faction how it was that I was diagnosed with sickle cell anaemia when I was a child.'

Aged nine, Carlos was unceremoniously whisked away from boarding school and hospitalised. Quaran-tined in bed behind drawn curtains, in fear and anxiety, he was sure he overheard the doctor saying, 'this child is febrile and anaemic.' What he discovered years later was that the doctor observing freckles on an olive skin child thought it an unusual occurrence. With a magnifying glass, to determine certainty, the Sherlock Holmes of the medical profession at Surrey's Small Fields Hospital may have assumed he was making a diagnosis that will create medical history. Sherlock Holmes had no Dr Watson to confirm his opinion. The trauma of the saga resonated with Carlos half a century later.

When the doctor's vernacular and demeanour changed, Carlos was delighted that he would be returning to school. Only to have his hopes dashed when the doctor's prescription was that 'the boy' not be allowed to, for fear of contaminating his peers. Bereft of choice, he reluctantly spent, and the Samuelson's grudgingly agreed, for him to recuperate at their residence in Wimbledon. This was the family that greeted him on arrival in England, who it was anticipated would keep an avuncular eye on him but persuaded the master that the seven-year neophyte is allowed to board a week before commencement of the school year. Inevitably, establishing the precedent for an already disadvantaged child to ridicule, jeered at mockingly, as someone who no-one wanted; 'a foreign boy lost in England.'

Nevertheless, the Samuelson family turned out unexpectedly to educate him to 'all things English.' That was what they would say to him with great regularity. But it was not of England he was being taught at school. Among the intellectual pursuits, Carlos was mesmerised with their eagerness to educate him about Judaism. Though he did not grasp the reason or purpose at the time, he was nevertheless by the age of twelve, and a year before leaving public school, generally interested in everything. So, any opportunity to spend time with an English family was a welcome relief from the bullying at school. In the first week of the month of his recuperation, Mr Samuelson told him that on Fridays the entire family, children and grandparents, celebrated Shabbat. Carlos was ready to participate, as to him, it was proof that he was now part of the family.

Back at school, with special weekends at Wimbledon, he was under strict instructions to be indoors on Fridays before sunset. Incrementally learning that Shabbat was a celebration by Jews commemorating the seventh day as a day of rest after the world was created in six days. At that age, what Carlos looked forward to most was their grandmother's cooking, superior to anything the school cooks ever dished out.

Reluctant to return to school after his allotted time for recovery, the school did not welcome him either. Carlos remembers those mean boys, for them it was open season to bully a 'sick foreign boy', which was to be his moniker. Insisting he had to take responsibility by the housemaster, he was inexplicably punished. He received the strap and endured detention with masters who were at times as mean as the boys. But he remembered being shouted at by the robust, fierce-looking sports master, that it was all 'character building.'

A year before leaving public school at thirteen, Carlos broke the rules and told the master about the bullying, injustice, and cruelty he was subjected to. Nothing was done about it, but he would come to learn that he was no exception. Exposition of cruelty has been documented by many prominent men who were boarders at public schools. Most realised that some masters seem to believe that the strap given as often as possible, and as cruel as possible, 'maketh a man.' With her undivided attention, Carlos felt he had been permitted to unburden himself of the years of loneliness and injustices he endured. Raving and ranting uncontrollably, for the first time he was unburdening himself. And he knew it would be the last time, as he subconsciously believed he had to wait for all those decades to tell the only person who cared. His Mother.

What the master, Mr Barnard, later said courteously, 'My dear boy, what does not kill you will make you stronger.' It was a reference to Carlos needing to pass the tongue twister, 'She sells, seashells, by the seashore,' which the boys required of him before he was allowed to enter the changing rooms to prepare for cricket; that most quintessentially English of games. At those and other occasions, Carlos recalled Tom Brown School Days, which the English Jesuit in Sao Paulo gave him saying it will prepare him for English Public School. In his many readings, he used to wonder if it did prepare its writer, Thomas Hughes?

Twelve-year-old Carlos' rescuer and forever-friend was a boy of means, who was not mean, but a purveyor of etiquette and good manners. Disparagingly referred to as 'Little Lord Fauntleroy,' he was the junior, John Bagwell Purefoy. The following five summers, with his sister reluctantly straggling along, herself a boarder at school in the New Forest in Hampshire, they traversed majestic woodlands, moorlands and crossed flowing streams on horseback, hiking or being driven and then driving a World War II utilitarian Land Rover owned by the local doctor. A man of the country and a great storyteller. Perennially dressed in tweeds and Wellington boots, visiting patients, and attending to the girls at boarding school. The locals affectionately referred to him as 'The Squire.' Many who knew, came to believe that Dr John Ratcliffe-Stewart influenced Carlos's choice of career and lifestyle.

The trios' explorations commenced soon after breakfast. Escaping from John and Caroline's industrialist father's summer residence in Fordingbridge, which lies at the northern end of the New Forest, with its fourteenth-century arched bridge spanning the River Avon. Rivers carried distinctly distant and tragic memories for Carlos which prohibited the children from swimming. Walking along the river, they went to Brockenhurst, which means 'Badgers Wood,' passing without reverence, St Nicholas church, the patron saint of travellers. These were among the places in the New Forest they knew and loved because, like the doctor, their mother Mrs Gillian Bagwell Purefoy, ensured these children were taught the history of the Forest and the responsibility for maintaining its pristine environment.

And in addition, the mother never failed to surreptitiously remind the children of the importance of observing good manners and etiquette in the villages, as they did at school and home. This was in preparation as they played in quaint little villages where 'little old ladies' needed assistance crossing the street. Children must also always observe the rule and 'offer to carry these ladies shopping.' And remember to never complain, no matter how heavy those bags were. Fond memories of endless cups of tea and cakes remained with all these children. For the first time, they were invited into old cottages, surrounded by neatly maintained gardens, and tiny rooms covered with doilies and laced curtained windows. They were cautioned 'not to snigger' when the old ladies pulled back the curtains at opportune moments, telling the children it was just to 'see what the neighbours were doing.' Tea with little old ladies, at little old cottages, were curtailed when the children refused to eat their 'greens' at dinner as they were well fed with scones and jam covered with cream as a reward for their good manners and good deeds.

History was not curtailed, it flowed as they lived it and learnt that forestation of the area was at the behest of King William, who in 1079 gave permission for the trees to be used in the building of Winchester Cathedral. The 'New Forest' was planted as a royal hunting ground. By 1086 the woods earnt its place in the eleventh century Domesday Book. Replete with history, buried in the churchyard in Lyndhurst was 'a certain Mrs Hargraves.' Lewis Carrol's inspirations for the character of Alice, on these children's favourite character from Alice in Wonderland. 'Now that is a history we know and love mother,' Caroline, would face-tiously say on occasions, having heard it more than once, and could because she was braver than the boys.

Doomsday was inevitable. But that came years later for the inseparable duo of the trio. Another Sunday. Another lunch. Followed on this special Sunday by his first formal meeting in the oak-panelled study of shelves creaking with musty books in an English industrialist home. Experiencing for the first time, a family endowed with means, in a residence in Weybridge, Surrey. Strategically located within commuting distance to London, at the mouth of the River Wey, a tributary of the Thames. Eager to be there, Carlos drove his British racing green MGB, GT and 'heeded no brook.'

Brimming with confidence, navigating a course to Weybridge, he would expertly accomplish with panache, as he was at the height of his motor racing training at Brands Hatch Motor Racing Circuit School in Kent. With boundless energy, enthusiasm, soaring ambition and in top gear, Carlos was determined to drive the Formula One circuits of the world. Encouraged and accompanied by Caroline on race days, he envisaged her being with him when he won a Formula One World Championship.

Lunch, however, was a nervous affair for him. Summoned, Carlos entered the study to find John senior, peering over bifocals across his cluttered highly polished English oak desk. Sheltering behind cigar smoke swirling in every direction seeking an escape. Here Carlos imagined he had been transported into a Dickensian atmosphere, with the smell of an establishment heritage study. With a wry smile, sensing the tension in the young man's entrapment, John Bagwell Purefoy mischievously said, 'My dear boy, should a married couple be frank and earnest.' Puzzled, 'Yes of course, of course, sir,' Carlos enthusiastically in naivety responded. Surely not, my boy, one of them must be a Gillian, Caroline or Mary,' drawing to Carlos attention the female gender and the women in his family.

Looking down on the dramatic performance, not as an audience, but as if to bear witness, was a large expensively adorned, heavy-framed, but slightly fading in the light, was a photograph, hanging above the fireplace. It was of one of his ancestors with a group of men in morning dress, standing on both sides of a seated Queen Victoria, quintessentially dressed in black. 'Was' Carlos would write in his journal, 'I a witness to a carefully staged scene or the practice of a lifetime of exercising the power of wealth and position.' Thinking, 'the boy' was not an equal or worthy of his daughter. To be told it was not an opinion shared by either his wife or daughter. Gillian, however, could never contradict her husband.

John Bagwell Purefoy was a man of his time, who closely observed time, from a family who in their time accumulated wealth from the exploits of The British East India Company. Carlos was sitting in front of a man who married a much younger attractive socialite, not economically endowed, but an epitome of elegance and sophistication. Devastated, foreboding what was to come, momentarily Carlos bit his lips to thwart tears, as he did not want to show vulnerability. Judgement delivered without much ado, Carlos was summarily dismissed in the tone that was perhaps used when irritated by the heat, scolding a punkahwallah, who he may have preferred to be deaf. A performance without applause but a bow to power when a blonde hair, blue-eyed English maiden was off to finishing school. Not Roedean in Sussex, as she was being prepared for as it was Gillian's alma mater, and preferred by her, but to school in the Swiss Alps.

John junior, when down from Oxford, would keep vigil with Carlos, who made his way along the river Thames from medical school to the Charles Dickens pub. A footpath John would come to regularly perambulate many years later as a Parliamentarian. Carlos' destiny was determined. He opted to traverse the globe in various incarnations. Caroline, on the other hand, graced European catwalks.

Years later Carlos would receive a cryptic note from her: 'I am just listening to Nights in White Satin, on Lanzarote.' One of the Spanish Canary Islands, about 500 kilometres (300 miles) from Madeira where, as children, the trio stayed at another of the family's holiday homes.

'Nights in white satin, never reaching the end. Letters I've written, never meaning to send......Just what the truth is I can't say anymore......Some try to tell me, thoughts they cannot defend... Just what you want to be, you will be in the end....'

A hit song in the 1970s written by Justin Hayward of the Moody Blues. Perhaps intended to confirm the rumours of her association with him or otherwise.

Olga Sara looked across the room at Carlos, both with tears freely flowing. She could not have known, and he could not have told her at other times. So, here and now he told stories she wanted to know. Not since he was seven, Carlos reverted to seeking comfort in his mother's arms, for their tears to saturate the pages of Cien anos de soledad (One

Hundred Years of Solitude) by Gabriel Garcia Marquez. Quickly closing the book, Carlos wanted to make history and preserve those salty pages.

Parenthetically, that book with tear-stained pages, stand in his study at Badgers Wood. Among his pantheon of Latin American literature, it holds pride of place, as it introduced him and the English-speaking world to magical realism. And indeed accompanied, by among others, the works of Isabel Allende, The House of the Spirits which resonated with mother and son because it paralleled aspects of their families' lives.

Carlos sought forgiveness. Revitalised in frailty, Olga Sara was ready to tell her story of those missing years. That was exactly what Carlos wished and waited for, for many years. She proceeded to tell her son she has been re-reading some of her favourite classic literature, preferring to read them in the language of the author. 'To have read Tolstoy and Dostoyevsky in Russian would have been a privilege indeed. And to think, we could have if only...,' as she smiled in reminiscence of fragmented memories, learnt vicariously not lived. Endow with Russian and Jewish first names, it was expected that she would have been able to, as her Jewish father spoke Russian, among other European languages.

Carlos offered coffee which he knew with certainty: black and must always be brewed with freshly ground Santos beans. With coffee brewing, he waited in silence listening to the gurgling and lingering in the distinct smell percolating the air that was forever Brazil for his mother. Memories and coffee brewing flooded the senses compelling him to sit at the piano making a fistful of it, in a clumsy attempt, as he played a bad rendition of a few notes of Eric Sate's first symphony. Olga Sara introduced Carlos to the piano which he gave up in preference for the guitar, telling her many years later that he could not carry a piano. A guitar is easier. For her, it was the fact that 'a piano demands more of you than a guitar.' But more importantly, she reminded him that his great grandmother Yolanda of the Braganza dynasty wrote in her journal that, 'the virtuosity of the piano, more than any other instrument, portrayed cultural sophistication.' Hearing those words for the first time sent shivers up his spine. This, he thought was said in a moment of weakness. Perhaps.

Without missing a beat, and exactly as she did when she taught him to play when he was five or six, Olga Sara sat next to her son and played how the composer intended. Stopping midway through playing, but still gently tinkling the ivories, declared, 'my favourite composer is not Eric Sate, my son, but Camille Saint-Saens.' Satiated with Santos coffee, his mother was prepared to tell him the true story.

Madeira, Saint-Saens acknowledged, had a profound impact on his compositions. The composer spent many summers there and waxed lyrical about the natural beauty of the island, as did Olga Sara with every opportunity. His composition, Carnival of Animals was inspired by the island. Olga Sara said in his pantheon of compositions, she preferred his piano recitals, but it was his organ compositions she most listened to growing up in Funchal. Unsurprisingly, she nevertheless said that her favourite composition of all time was Beethoven symphony number nine, 'which as you know', she avers, 'ends with Ode to Joy.' Replying, 'as you taught me, all music is an ode to joy.' Carlos acknowledged that her knowledge of classical music was superior to his. For which she expressed disappointment that he did not appear to want to correct.

Searching for comfort, she resorted to recline in her favourite armchair, covering her legs as if to camouflage her frailty. For her, that old worn and faded green and gold embroidered blanket she made of Brazil's national colours, showing her true colours. In the room, she was surrounded predominantly by her Portuguese heirlooms and memorabilia carefully arranged on the tops of tables covered with her great grandmother's embroidery and paintings of the Empire hanging on walnut walls.

Olga Sara's lucidity of spirit was remarkable as was her response to Carlos' soliloquy and the events in the order of delivery. Within hallowed atmosphere verging on seraphic inspiration, the timing seemed to be in synchronicity with the standing wall clock. Handed down through generations, and known for its gold pendulum and irregular chiming, a testimony of its weariness from longevity. Sunk in the depth of expectation, Carlos waited for the chime to queue her in. 'You are an intelligent boy and with your experience in medicine, you know that sickle cell anaemia only afflicts people of African ancestry.' Keeping the momentum, 'I know mother,' Carlos replied, 'and that is exactly why I am asking: you are Portuguese, and Dad was Brazilian of Portuguese and Tupi Indian ancestry.' Pugnaciously, after decades of waiting, Carlos retorted, 'How do you know we do not have African ancestry? Should we not find out?'

With a sigh of resignation and determination of pride, Olga Sara gently lifted her downcast head as the light was dimming in her eyes, exposing her sadness in full. Purposeful with intention, her story was of the silence in solitude, memories of sailing ships disappearing on the horizon in distant centuries. Gazing through a fog of mystery with regret, eliciting anguish, and despair in Portuguese. She religiously believed emotions were best expressed in romance languages. English was best used for commerce. The light faded as she slipped into a labyrinth of hallucination about her family's dynastic prophesy.

Abruptly interrupting the conversation, Carmelita Evora dos Barros Lopez called out entering the room, 'Mae. Mae' (mother, mother) with her husband Ernesto in tow, as always, rushing to share her well-worn warm greetings of hugs and multiple kisses. Realising she had interrupted something, as the room emitted tension, she apologised, as she felt time was not on anyone's side. She nevertheless asked, 'what is wrong?'

Pretending to know, or perhaps she simply did not want to, turned away gesticulating, 'let us cook.' Looking questioningly at Ernesto she said cryptically, 'why haven't you opened the wine.' With eyes fixed on her mother, proclaimed, 'It is your favourite Madeira wine mother.' Olga Sara looked at her and with Carlos in her peripheral vision, gently shook her head from side to side. He thought. 'I know; like mother, like daughter.'

But instead thought of injecting some levity into the conversation and said, 'have some Madeira, m'dear.' English coined indeed. Perfectly timed as her son G. Rupert Evora dos Barros and his wife Marie joined the celebration of witnessing a life fading in their presence. Unannounced, as notice or invitation is seldom required to her home, which soon transformed into a celebration with multitudes. Olga Sara, rejuvenated, welcomed with blessings the global food flavours and ambience of what was to pass for a fiesta in which the assembled purposely concealed bereavement in an atmosphere of denial.

Exhaustion crept in on Carlos and sleep beckoned. Taking his leave with salutations of boa noite, obrigado, (good night, thanks) he surprised himself and everyone else with his eloquence. In a Portuguese milieu it came naturally and pleased them all, bringing a moment of levity. At that precise moment, the transmutation was mesmeric through nostalgia in that ambience, he had not experienced before. Transmuted in spirituality to a time, a seven-year-old vividly remembering saying goodbye to a place and family assembled during crises and celebrations. Portuguese and Brazilian dishes, music, and laughter, always the antidote.

Mesmerised, Carlos dreamt of a past and a mother's

love lost in visions and tales of sailing ships disappearing over the horizon, sails emblazoned with the Red Cross of The Order of Christ. A past she chose not to remember, or it was too painful to divulge. Instead, she painstakingly confided in her journals and epistolary persona for over seven decades. Stashed away in her ancient and battered seafarer's treasure chest in her box room of odds and sods where she alone spent many, many hours.

Handmade of Brazilwood with Portuguese cork used as its base to preserve it from being damaged by saltwater. That chest had the hallmark of a family heirloom. It bore the fading emblem of the Order of Christ disappearing into the wood, but detectable with fingertips was EVORA. Given to her mother, Lia Maria, by Olga Sara's great grand-father, a relic of the eighteenth century of his great grand-father Dom Paulo de Oliveira Evora.

The chest held the legend of centuries built on real and fabricated stories which evolved into secrets over many lifetimes. On the top of the chest was a sturdy iron latch with a heavy brass lock. All custodians had to observe the rule, which was to always keep the chest locked. Resulting in preserving secrets with a faint but distinct odour of spices, predominantly cloves and nutmeg from the entrepot of Malacca in Malaysia, which the Portuguese Empire controlled.

With that chest, Carlos finally learnt that there will no longer be 'unfinished business.' Appropriately and timely in her honour, he thought, as he looked at her lying in bed drifting on celestial clouds. Surrounded by her children, in her room enveloped with scented candles strategically placed as if to flicker in the gentlest of breeze as she intermittently gazed at them and Tampa bay. Olga Sara saw their quizzical look and pre-empted Carmelita and Rupert's question. 'Carlos will tell you.' Mother and son subscribed to Plato's dictum: An unexamined life is not worth living.

Whispering to Carlos, with voice failing as she was drifting, 'Come a little bit closer, hear what I have to say. It is getting late otherwise you will dream my life after I pass away.' There is a saying, 'If you do not release what is hidden inside, it will destroy you. If you liberate it, it will bring salvation.' Then she ordered him to promise to take her to Portugal. 'I tried not to live in the past, but the past lives in me.' Tearing up, 'I will mother,' said Carlos, wondering, he would write, 'will we know her story by then?' He was, and perhaps so was his brother and sister, also thinking that they can now unearth the true history of a family that had done much and said little. Instead, they confided in journals, letters, and drawings. The purpose of searching through these artefacts was not to reclaim the past but to understand its impact on the future.

Approaching midnight, with the procession of visitors temporarily farewelled, the orphans, as their sister now called them, reflected on their circumstances. Orphans of a few hours in time but not in spirit, they made their way to their mother's garden, which like all her other gardens, was her sanctuary. With its neat row of English box hedge and roses, not in bloom in Autumn, but an outline of her design could still be appreciated by candlelight on a moonless night. At any time, night or day, Olga Sara would be seen there reminiscing in her solitude in the wonders of creation of plants transported with nature's blessings which could still display lavish colours and fragrances.

Surrounded by lilac scented candles belching smoke, sporadically mingling, and lingering above them waiting for her presence. Fumes spiralled out of green mosquito coils eager to join the smoke haze to complete the medley, with the sweetened tinge of smoke spiralling from Rupert's Cuban cigar. Juxtaposed between light and darkness, silence fell. Spontaneously, a cloud of multicoloured smoke hovered, blanketing the sky foreboding ancestral imagery of ships in full sail on journeys of exploration to create a dynasty, now disappearing in a puff of smoke, leaving nothing but ashes. Spirited by the heightened tension, Carmelita surely heard the melliferous sound of her mother's voice as she gazed at the drifting clouds and cascading smoke forming a recognisable image taking heavenly flight in a divine apparition.

Perhaps it was a result of the concatenation of events. But the act of observation does change reality. Carlos vowed to himself 'to expect the unexpected.' With candour, for the first time, the three orphans voiced their realisation in their awakening: they did indeed know less about their mother and her family than they thought.

Now with God-given right, it was their opportunity to know their family history, as it is best written by orphans. Home alone, watched over by his mother peering over his shoulders, Carlos dreamt of it in the decade of writing.

Proud owners of the seafarers' treasure chest, once hidden from the light, was waiting in silence as dark rolling clouds disappeared to another hemisphere to make way for dawn to break on Tampa Bay. An eagerness in abeyance, they thought, and then believed that the treasure chest could be their family's Pandora's box. Perhaps. Bringing light to the darkness may reveal the truth. Their fear was of becoming captives of their mother and perpetuating the nostalgia, handing it down to the next generation. With unspoken realisation, simultaneously in furious agreement, they committed to a journey to trace the story of their dynasty.

From what they would come to discover, it became evident that significant historical changes are achieved by informally organised groups, but when officially documented, revolutionary changes are thinly veiled. The de Oliveira Evora family rose to prominence in the era when Portugal was an Empire. Their quest of centuries to build a dynasty resulted in their lives being intertwined with the rise and fading power of the empire, paralleling its contradictions. Clearly, the Empire made them, and they made the Empire. Both were about people's ambitions and places. One cannot be understood without the other.

THE
PORTUGUESE
EMPIRE

PORTUGAL

THE FIRST MODERN EMPIRE

'To arms, to arms, over the land, over the sea.'
(EXTRACT FROM THE NATIONAL ANTHEM)

The de Oliveira Evora family traced their origins to that small Western European country on the Iberian Peninsula. Like Portugal, the family's distinctive past was replete with tragedy and triumph. The country's history was intertwined with that of Spain. Both occupied by Islamic North Africa and influenced by its Jewish community.

Other European countries were also influential in Portugal's role in the world. None more so than England, with which it had a complex and bewildering partnership which at times was paternalistic, disruptive with failed attempts to subjugate Portugal's national interests. Astonishingly, over six centuries ago, these countries signed treaties with each other before doing so with other countries. Remarkably with expectations that they will also be honoured in the modern world.

Although the English and Flemish Monarchies received public acclamation and binding treaties in return for their assistance; the Knights Templar did not. It was just expected of them. The Knights were Christian noblemen warriors who fought to keep all of Europe and the Holy Land of Jerusalem safe for Christianity.

Throughout the occupation, the Knights' goal for Portugal was to restore the country to its original status. To achieve this objective, they continuously fought the Moors from the stronghold of the walled city they built at Tomar. From their medieval castles, immense and unquestionable wealth, they reigned supreme in Portugal as in other Catholic European countries.

By the twelfth century, the Templars' immense wealth made them the most influential institution in all Christendom and the leaders of the Crusades which started with them guarding Europeans on their pilgrimage to the Holy Land. The French King Phillipe saw their immense wealth as a solution to his financial problems. The crisis over the Templars culminated in a stoush of medieval proportions between the Pope and European monarchs against the French king. Despite the long drawn out saga, the Pope reluctantly succumbed to the abolition of the Templars.

With papal approval, the king could now denigrate their principles and practices with legitimacy, putting members of the Order to the stake and seizing their wealth. Most of these accusations were proven to be false or simply fabricated. This fiasco did not affect the Templars in Portugal as the Church and Monarchy fought against the Pope, pointing out their crusading role in the Reconquista.

Reprieved in Portugal, the Knights Templar changed their name to the Order of Christ and the monarchy agreed to them retaining all their property and maintain the privileges granted to the Templars.

At the request of the Monarchy, which historically colluded with the Catholic Church, the Pope agreed that the Order would finance and manage the expeditions to spread Christianity to the new world. The Order, therefore, played a significant role in the development of the Empire. It funded explorations, as was evident by ships' sails emblazoned with a Red Cross, which was the Order's emblem. The Templars worked with the Jewish community, which financed global projects such as the building of ships, forts and cities in the colonies. As a result of these activities and their management of the pilgrimage to the Holy Land, the Templars were credited with developing the banking industry or at least contributing to its genesis.

Tomar remained the seat of their power. It was built on Roman ruins in a gothic Manueline style. The Castle was a magnificent representation of the wealth and privileges the Order attained and the esteem in which it was held. Reaching greater heights, however, could not be imagined. But it did when Prince Henry the Navigator became the Master of the Order.

All these factors contributed to the period of exploration which began in the fifteenth century and gave rise to the legend of 'Henry the Navigator.' The first overseas expansion that he led resulted in the capture of Ceuta in Morocco and most of North Africa. Prince Henry (Henrique) was the son of King Joao I and his English wife Philippa of Lancaster. This marriage consolidated the close and significantly enduring relationship between England and Portugal. Other marriages between the English and Portuguese monarchies followed until the Portuguese monarchy was abolished in the early twentieth century.

For Portugal, the fifteenth century was referred to as its 'Marvellous Century.' The reasons were multifaceted. As a country with few natural resources, which they needed for development, Portugal was compelled to look beyond its shores. Spain was not an option, but the Atlantic Ocean which lapped its shores was to be charted and lands seized, and inhabitants converted to Christianity. The Portuguese observed and learnt from the Moors during the occupation. With resources and skilled craftsmen from the Islamic world, they built significant infrastructure which modernised Portugal. It propelled Portugal to explore trade routes to acquire gold and to outflank the Islamic world by sailing around Africa attacking Islamic centres to convert them to Christianity.

Stifled during the period of Moorish rule, once unshackled the Portuguese wanted to break the Venetian monopoly over the spice trade. The desire was to acquire supplies directly from the East, rather than paying exorbitant prices for products essential for preserving food at home and for the navigators' extended sea voyages. It was no easy feat, as the Genoese were renowned for being great sailors. They established trading posts along the Atlantic and Mediterranean and subsequently even in Lisbon. All of which the Portuguese wanted to displace.

To achieve its objectives, Portugal created a network of oceanic trade routes that contributed to rapidly transforming the global economy. The overseas expansion which began as a commercial enterprise ended up with Portugal creating an Empire. And through its discoveries, according to the prominent economic historian, Professor Niall Ferguson, the Portuguese changed the modern world and became the first modern Empire. Other European countries followed and started the colonisation of large swathes of the world. A leader in colonisation, Portugal had colonies in parts of Africa, Asia, and South America.

The Monarchy and the Church influenced the granting of contracts for the spice trade and indeed permission to settle the colonies. Payment to both institutions and influence in the Church was the determining factor as the Monarchy depended on advice from the Church which led to collusion by these institutions. Prominent Establishment families and those with sons in religious orders received preferential treatment. The de Oliveira Evora family's record shows it was granted permission to engage in the spice trade because family members were in the Order of the Society of Jesus. Commonly known as Jesuits, they were not only religious men but explorers and builders of Empires.

Over centuries, members of the de Oliveira Evora family were Jesuits. They facilitated contracts which led the family to engage in the spice trade in the seventeenth century. It was a period when competition between European countries intensified leading to Spain and Portugal agreeing to diversify their products. The Spanish Conquistadors were now fully-fledged raiders for gold, no longer committed spice traders. Spain's obsession with pillaging gold from South America gave rise to a myth which persists. El Dorado, that fabled city of gold, is featured in the national anthem or folklore of these countries for the past five centuries.

Not to compete with Spain, the Portuguese experimented with agricultural products such as wheat and sugar cane in its mid-Atlantic island colonies of Madeira and the Azores. The de Oliveira Evora family were early settlers in the former colony through marriage and business relationship with the Braganza family who were given the mandate to settle the island. With fertile soil, agricultural products could be grown all year round to supply Europe, which was a one-season crop producer. Overwhelmed by demand settlers soon realised that Portugal could not supply enough labourers to meet the growing markets at home and the rest of Europe. The solution was to copy the well-established practice of the Islamic and Mediterranean countries.

Although the Portuguese initiated the Atlantic slave trade, they did not invent slavery. It was an ancient practice which the Islamic world turned into fine art, and the Portuguese copied the practice. With agility and alacrity, the Portuguese adopted their sailing ships to transport people from their West Africans colonies to Europe and then North and South America. It is unquestionable, records show the Figueira and de Oliveira Evora families sourced slaves for Portugal and Madeira and perhaps the Azores. Madeira is a certainty as they had a monopoly to supply slaves to the island which was a fiefdom of the Braganza fraternity.

Portugal, therefore, replaced trading spices with trading people. Of which it became unscrupulous and rapacious. Unsurprisingly, it was economically more lucrative than spices. Other Portuguese spice traders reconfigured and refitted their sailing ships to transport people too. To be more productive in this growing and exceedingly lucrative trade, a new type of vessel had to be built. It presented opportunities for new family businesses that were not yet well established in the spice trade. Their advantage was not having to incur costly refitting but to build ships customised for trafficking people. These new vessels quickly became more competitive, monopolising the route between Africa and South America. Traders in people are referred to as 'people traffickers' in contemporary society.

These new developments, including an unlimited supply of free labourers, led Portugal to consolidate its position by developing lands it colonised. The Empire family businesses were monopolies, for which they paid tributes to the

Monarchy and the Church. The latter was a more significant beneficiary as families also paid indulgence, to reduce
punishment for sins. Despite paying exorbitant, or perhaps
because of it, these business monopolies became rapacious
and the families' wealth grew with assets at home and in
all the colonies. Accumulating wealth became an obsession
with boundless opportunities for slave labour. These plantations were all year-round operations as were the growing
European markets. These immensely profitable businesses
propagated a culture of privilege and 'a born to rule' hubris
that has prevailed for centuries in former colonies, most
evident in Brazil.

As late as the 1880s, just before slavery was reluctantly
abolished in Brazil, Portugal argued vociferously that it
had only colonised unoccupied lands. What it did was to
ignore the presence of the native people. Allowing it to
establish enclaves in countries to building forts which had
small Portuguese settlements. None of this was supposedly
forcefully done as they always tried to negotiate agreements. Once that was achieved, however, they did set about
making significant changes in these places. Never seeking
but certainly ignoring the inhabitants' objections.

The central reason was to transform these colonies
so that Portuguese sailors and missionaries could feel 'at
home.' Replicating the architecture of Lisbon, establishing
the Portuguese lifestyle, and converting the local inhabitants to Christianity were priorities. And as beneficiaries,
they served the institutions and patrons well once they

were left to their own devices such as assuming the status of *Senhjores* (gentlemen). Uneducated sailors adopted a corrupted lifestyle based on behaviour which imitated their superiors, vicariously learnt from what they saw in the streets of Lisbon or their villages. Misrepresenting men of the status of the de Oliveira Evora through objectification was harshly dealt with, to thwart pomposity.

With reports of peasant soldiers parading as gentlemen, abusing colonised peoples, the Monarchy agreed to establish the municipal system of Lisbon to manage the colonies. The Church agreed that the responsibility was to be given to the Order of the Society of Jesus, or Jesuits, who therefore became the harbingers of the Catholic Church in the Empire. To demonstrate their fealty to the Pope and usurp the Spanish, the Portuguese built the first church and cathedral in Salvador in Brazil and established the first diocese in South America. The Order of the Society of Jesus was emboldened and became more active, expanding its developmental programs, when it received the imprimatur of the Pope. Salvadorians did not object as they benefitted from the trade and education delivered by Jesuits.

Despite its avowed policies that forts on its trading routes were not to be imposed or militarised, Portugal acted against its avowed declarations. Frontier wars in Europe with Spain and France, and over the colonies, and internal conflict, led Portugal to put armed soldiers at trading posts to protect shipping and its colonies, effectively militarising all the lands it occupied. These activities took a heavy toll on the

Portuguese government's finance, leaving it in debt to inter-national money lenders who were predominantly European Jewry.

TRAFFICKING PEOPLE

With royal assent and Jewish finance, families such as the Braganza and de Oliveira Evora were still able to run profitable businesses despite the country's financial crises. This was also the case with other families in the city of Evora who also owned some of the most successful slave-trading businesses. The city boasted many successful entrepreneurs. Dom Tristao Homen, a nobleman who also traded slaves and even had slaves on his estate in Evora. Municipal records identified others in the business network such as Brites Figueira and Donna Ana Ataide. Initially, they auctioned slaves in Lisbon and sent them to Madeira as agricultural workers, and indeed to the United States and Asia.

Auctioning slaves in Portugal were infrequent except when Africans' wealthy families needed slaves as domestic servants and agricultural labourers. With such a diverse group and activities in their network, it would be surprising if the de Oliveira Evora did not also have slaves in their homes in Lisbon and Evora. But with no archival record or journal entry, leading to the conclusion that it was a common practice which did not warrant mention.

Evidence that trading African slaves were more lucrative than spices was readily available through the established networks. Published and archival records of return on investment of seven hundred percent made attracting Jewish investors easier. In fact, European Jewish investors were plentiful, making transporting people one of their most profitable investments. Portuguese families from the city of Evora had all the aces to profit from this trade: Jewish money, support from the Nobility and the Church, leadership in navigation technology and the military to be available as their private armies. Collusion between all these parties was assured once they were handsomely rewarded.

A confluence of opportunities arose for Portugal with colonies on both sides of the Atlantic. Transportation was shorter and therefore quicker from West Africa to Northeast Brazil making it the most profitable trade route. And once Portuguese settlers found that the northeast region of Brazil was perfect for agriculture, the price and demand for slaves increased significantly.

Africans were transported to Salvador in Northeast Brazil in preference to Europe, and North America. The abundant supply of slave labour transformed Brazil into 'the greatest plantation' in South America. It was estimated that Portuguese traders transported approximately twelve million Africans across the Atlantic from its colonies. Of which, five million were brought to Brazil and sold in Rio de Janeiro and Salvador.

As a result, *Sao Salvador da Bahia de Todos os Santos* (Holy Saviour of the bay of All Saint) was Brazil's first capital, built predominantly by slaves. It was also one of the most lucrative trading hubs in South America, as the bay was also an active whaling station. Maritime records show that Salvador was regularly congested with European sailing ships loading and unloading all types of products, people, and whale oil which was produced in the bay, making it a significant exporter of the product.

In the bay, the steady arrival of ships caused significant congestion as they waited to unload people captured for the ships' owners. Unfortunately, many died on the sailing ships on the journey from Africa, a result of overcrowding, heat exhaustion and disease. Speculation that 'thousands, if not hundreds of thousands' died as a result cannot be verified as there are no records available in Lisbon, Salvador or anywhere else in Brazil. Salvador's reason is that a major fire in the city in the nineteenth century destroyed all the records. Nevertheless, slave traders and European governments were prepared to acknowledge reports 'that hundreds of slaves died under these conditions.'

Changing European geopolitics and reverberations, a result of the Enlightenment, led to the era of colonisation reaching its zenith in the early nineteenth century. By then Portuguese colonist families had accumulated immense wealth through land ownership all over the Empire. Land was allocated to them over centuries by the monarchy, the Church and Portuguese and Brazilian government. Land was also stolen through displacing the native population, land grabbing, squatting and indeed unequal treaties.

Portugal's reassessment of its massive and disparate empire encouraged families to also reassess their global businesses. The de Oliveira Evora and Braganza family businesses consolidated their holdings in Portugal, Madeira, and Brazil. Others such as the Figueria family were more thinly spread in the colonies.

All these factors in combination contributed to the decline of the Portuguese Empire. Noticeably, it started to wane in the late nineteenth century when there was also an outcry for the abolition of slavery. Advocated, not by the beneficiaries or parliamentarians, but initiated by the Quakers and women artists, who were also credited as the early painters of African women slaves. They believed 'slavery was dividing the nations and the world.' William Wilberforce, a member of the British Parliament, took up the cudgels. After a vociferous and lengthy campaign, legislation to abolish slavery was promulgated on 26 July 1833. Wilberforce died on 29 July 1833. To expedite the process, the Rothchild banking behemoth, financed the British government to compensate slave owners. This incident, among others, contributed to the sarcasm, 'Money is the god of our time, and Rothschild is his prophet.'

Unlike its close ally, the Portuguese government under the Marquis of Pombal refused to debate abolition. Possibly because there was no groundswell, in a staunchly Catholic country. The legislation was not for abolition. Rather, it was to prohibit the forced importation of Africans, proclaiming: 'any enslaved person brought to Portugal would be freed.'

Squarely and deliberately, it was aimed at stopping the transport of any more Africans to Portugal, which was already sending slaves from Portugal to Madeira.

The government was also determined to stop the new young breed of entrepreneurial investors, hell-bent on participating in a get rich scheme which was being pursued by neophytes to make as much money as quickly as possible. Legislation and a desire not to have Africans in Lisbon contributed to the cessation of the practice. Bringing slaves to Lisbon ceased. Complying with the legislation, the established trading families focussed on refitting ships and expanding agricultural plantations to exporting products, especially sugar, from the colonies.

Brazil continued to benefit from the now more lucrative business of the slave trade, as there were no new competitors. For Brazil, the abolition of slavery was complicated and self-serving. Landowners effectively controlled all levels of government and were owners of large businesses. Enormously influential, they determined the country's policy. More importantly, *manumissions* (the freeing of slaves by their owners) would not be approved unless they were compensated by the State. The complication was that they effectively 'owned' the State, as they were the major taxpayers, unless they were tax evaders, as they inevitably were.

Britain and Portugal tried unsuccessfully to influence Brazil to institute abolition. To force the case, British and Portuguese men-of-war patrolled the Atlantic between

Africa and Brazil. It was a classic case of hypocrisy as the Portuguese economy was dependant on money paid by the Brazilian treasury and Portuguese who owned plantations in Brazil but reside in Portugal. Slavery, however, was finally abolished in Brazil on 13th May 1888, making it the last country to implement the legislation. Slavery may have been abolished, but its legacy cast a long shadow over the country. It entrenched landowning families' control of Brazil and contributed to social injustice and condemned families to generations of poverty.

Brazil, although by then an independent country, was still a significant contributor to the Portuguese economy. That realisation led the Portuguese government in the nineteenth century to undertake a thorough evaluation of its Empire with the sole purpose of assessing the colonies' contribution to its economy. The verdict was that the value of the African colonies was based on sourcing people for the slave trade. Goa, the enclave in India, was ranked as invaluable as its economic contribution far outweighed its size.

Madeira was highly ranked as an economic asset. Initially, the island's assets were sugar and wheat, but by the late eighteenth century, it had become a global brand synonymous with wine. Additionally, the port in Funchal, Madeira's capital, became a major hub for ships sailing between Portugal and Brazil. Most importantly, Madeira had never been classified as a colony. Rather, it had been incorporated into Portugal as a municipality of Lisbon. Most of its residents were Portuguese with a small percentage of the population who were African slaves and those of mixed race.

The crowning glory of the empire was Brazil with its enormous landmass and assets, such as minerals. without which Portugal would not have been ranked as a major Empire. The Portuguese government's colonial review resulted in other colonies receiving less attention. Many were unprepared but were granted independence as they became too costly for Lisbon to maintain. On gaining independence, the population of inhabitants who were Portuguese nationals or descendants of Portuguese settlers moved to Brazil or Portugal. Simultaneously, it deprived these former colonies of a professional and business class, leaving them with a legacy of poverty. Yet these former colonies contributed to Portugal's development resulting in Lisbon, by the eighteenth century, being described as 'the most beautiful city in Europe.'

LISBON IN LIGHT AND DARKNESS

Bearing several nomenclatures, 'the city by the sea' gained currency and continues to be used to describe Lisbon. Its heyday was indeed during the period of the Empire when the Monarchy and the Catholic Church ruled supreme and families connected to both institutions grew rich on trading spices and then on trading people. All these factors contributed to making Lisbon the first global city and by the seventeenth century Europe's first multicultural metropolis.

The de Oliveira Evora family members' journal entries waxed lyrical about 'a bustling port city on the Tagus river frenzied with the activity of sailing ships bringing spices, products and materials from the colonies.' The most valuable turned out to be gold which was ironical as the Spanish king who named the river allegedly declared its sands were covered with gold. A century and a half later, African slaves replaced spices which kept the port busy for a shorter period. Frenzied with development, the port was again bustling with activity. This time it was with locally quarried marble, sculptured and patterned tiles designed with tropical images, shipped to the colonies to replicate Portuguese architecture so that administrators, priests and sailors would always feel as if they were still living in Lisbon.

Lisbon's status as the capital of the Empire ebbed and flowed through four centuries which included European wars, as Portugal fought battles with its neighbours to maintain its status and strategic position as a colonial power and a major port. Its rivalry with Spain and Holland continued until the First World War which also marked the official dissolution of the empire and monarchy. Brazil took the opportunity to declare independence. Incrementally, other colonies fought wars of independence or were granted independence when they were no longer an economic asset to Portugal.

With its Empire in decline and the monarchy in decay, Portugal became a republic in 1910. From then until 1926 the country and many of its colonies entered a period of political instability and economic degradation. Regular changes of government and incompetent self-serving elite families held sway in every aspect of Portuguese society. Lisbon remained the centre of power. Continued social upheaval and economic stagnation finally propelled the military, supported by the Church and elite families, to seize political power. The governing military regime gave priority to economic development.

To execute its economic policy, the regime appointed Antonio de Oliveira Salazar, a professor of economics at the University of Coimbra, the country's oldest and most prestigious educational institution. His appointment would come to mark a turning point for the country during his four decades in office.

From humble beginnings in an agriculture region, Salazar was educated by Jesuits and decided to enter the Order. Finding that it did not meet his expectations, he went to university and taught at a school run by Canon Barreiros modelled on an English Public School. The English education system had such a profound impact on Salazar that he described it as the best in Europe. Declaring: 'the Iberian school system could not equip men to meet what is needed to develop and modernise Portugal.'

Salazar also had life-long respect for the British system of government. Yet he had a turbulent relationship with successive British governments. Similarly, his relationship was fractious with British investors in the wine and other industries in the Portuguese empire, specifically on the island of Madeira. Salazar was overwhelmingly supported by the old established families who benefitted from auto-cratic governments over many centuries. For them, little needed to be changed.

In 1940 Salazar became President of Portugal. Consid-ered more an academic than a politician, he assembled a government experienced in the political machinations of Europe. Supported by the military, the Church, elite fami-lies, and complemented by a diplomatic corps of seasoned professionals, some who carried vestiges of the monarchy. Making them attuned to Imperial European lifestyle but predominantly Anglophiles, leaving an impression of a government well equipped to serve the nation during turbulent times. Credited for ushering in a period of stability and economic development; it was achieved by harsh measures. It included the imposition of dictatorial legislation overlooked by the establishment who benefitted most from the policies of his administration.

How fortuitous it was that Portugal had highly skilled diplomats when the second World War threatened to subjugate all of Europe to Hitler's Germany. Cunningly, Salazar used the provision of a weakened economy to declare neutrality. Accordingly, his statement to the country reads: "It was the only option for a poor country with an ill-equipped military and predominantly agrarian economy, with a high percentage of the population illiterate, and with poor infrastructure."

These were compelling reasons for the policy of neutrality. But there were historical agreements between Portugal and the United Kingdom, which was in place and had to be honoured. Salazar argued that abiding by it could destroy the economy. There was also Portugal's responsibility to the sizeable British expatriate community in Lisbon and the country's second city of Oporto. They were predominantly in business and had developed and managed the wine and port business in Oporto and Madeira. Portugal needed to retain and hence protect the wine and port industry for its economic survival.

Salazar's dilemma was how to satisfy British demands and its citizens' expectations. Preserving neutrality would become a major challenge. There was significant pressure from the British government, concern about Spain's historical relationships and border control, and importantly its well-established trading relationship with Germany.

Weighing the options in this dilemma, astonishingly, the president intervened in the country's culture, deciding to establish rules on how the Portuguese should conduct themselves in neutrality. Summing up his opinion of what he expected of the people:

> 'We do not discuss God and virtue; we do not discuss
> the nation and its history; we do not discuss authority,
> and its prestige; we do not discuss family and its morals;
> we do not discuss the glory of work and its duty.'
> (Nogueira 1977, 368)

Tussling with these pressures and internal dissent, which placed Salazar in a predicament, hardened his resolve to remain neutral. Portugal's centrality to the war efforts was not only its geographic location on the Atlantic but its supply of Tungsten (*wolfran*). This mineral mined in Portugal was essential to the manufacture of weaponry. Therefore, it was highly sought after during the war. Before the war, Portugal had been exporting the mineral to England and Germany. Salazar realised that the mineral was both an asset and a liability. Reports from meetings the president and his administration held with the business community and financiers noted their nervousness as the country was a target for an invasion to access the mineral. The fear of these meetings being reported by the press led the government to tightly control the press. Salazar did not want to alarm the population.

Compounding this predicament, Jewish refugees had begun using Lisbon as a staging post to escape to North and South America and Palestine. This situation made Portugal further vulnerable. Increasingly, intelligence reports were of a German invasion to seize control of tungsten and deport refugees to concentration camps.

Pressure on the Portuguese government was relentless over the supply of tungsten. Germany and Britain carried out significant propaganda campaigns countering each other's presence in Lisbon and keeping the country on constant alert which contributed to the size and increased power of the spy agency and police force. Spies from both countries tried to influence Salazar, government officials, and the secret police, with threats and bribes.

In neutrality, the port of Lisbon on the Tagus river leading to the Atlantic, developed a significant entrepot becoming Portugal's asset as it was the gateway to the United States and South America, especially as neither of these continents was at that stage engaged in the war. In a quandary, Portugal realised it was inadequately prepared for the consequences of its strategic position. And neither were the Establishment and business community. Both strongly supported Salazar and propagated his government's policies.

By the late nineteenth century, the de Oliveira Evora had already built a global business. It consisted of a well-established network of Jewish financiers at home and in London and assets in Portugal, Brazil, and Madeira. All the families' business interests in the former Empire was personal. Supporting Salazar, they also endeavoured to do whatever was necessary to protect their wealth and global network which made them vulnerable as it was multidimensional and multicultural. Financed by Jewish finance became their principle concern.

Refugees fleeing occupied Europe in 1939 were initially predominantly from Germany, Austria, and Poland, but within two years it was from all over occupied Europe. For them, neutral Lisbon was the gateway to the US, South America, and Palestine. This resulted in Lisbon undergoing significant structural development. With a rapidly increasing population, infrastructure had to be built, with accommodation a priority. The hospitality industry rapidly expanded resulting in a vibrant nightlife, earning Lisbon the moniker: 'The City of Lights,' as other European cities operated underground and in darkness to escape German night bombing.

In the hustle and bustle, little consideration was given to the significant disruption to the lives of *Lisboetas* and the established expatriate communities. Wealthy and famous European and Americans gravitated to Lisbon for its nightlife. Lisbon night clubs and the Grand Estoril casino, just outside Lisbon, were major attractions unhindered by the war. The casino was compared to its counterpart in the movie *Casablanca;* from where some of the activities were drawn. The only exception was the Estoril casino was grander than Rick's café.

The movie, released in November 1942, may well have been reflecting Lisbon. Casablanca was described as 'cinematic magic which occurred accidentally on purpose.' Adapted from a play written by Murray Burnett and Joan Alison, it was based on Burnett's experiences travelling in Europe in 1938 when antisemitism was rampant.

Directed by Michael Curtiz, a Hungarian Jew, he anglicised his name and personally selected the cast who reflected his experience of the multi-ethnic cities of Western Europe. Most of the approximately hundred actors were recent refugees to the US, and some had passed through Lisbon. Like Curtiz, many also lost families in concentration camps, making the movie reflect 'the exile condition with uncommon poignancy.' All members of the crew spoke pidgin English. So Curtiz, having been mocked for his accent, placed a sign over his door during the shooting of the movie: 'Curtain spoken here!'

Most of the refugees arriving in Lisbon had an arduous journey. Fighting and risking everything to escape the European pogroms where they would face certain death in concentration camps. For them, it was a time of sheer desperation. An entry in the de Oliveira Evora journal stated: *'Desperate people in desperate times.'* Knowing what was occurring, refugees were being prevented from entering

THE PORTUGUESE LADY'S EARRINGS

Portugal. Entry was only granted to those who had an exit visa which guaranteed officials that they could enter Palestine, North and South America. Going to another European country was not possible as these countries, such as Britain potentially faced invasion and argued vociferously that it could no longer cope with refugees. This caused significant problems for the Portuguese government as Britain pressured it to grant entry to Jewish refugees. Salazar's intransigence and displeasure with being pressured to change his policy was reflected by government officials and some ministers. But not the sophisticated diplomats and many of the country's global business community.

Diplomats in Portuguese embassies and consulates who issued visas to refugees were accused of disobeying the law, which was highly suspect and contestable as there was no law prohibiting diplomats from performing their duties. Rather, it was undoubtedly a reflection of antisemitism in government, its lingering fear of Germany's overtly brazen subversive activity and the threat of invasion. Diplomats who persisted in sending refugees to Portugal were dismissed from their positions in France, which was the centre of the activity.

Summoned from consulates, these diplomats were ostracised by government officials and from any further official positions and social circles. Many never served their country again and were disenfranchised. Post-war recognition of them as heroes for saving the lives of Jews came too late for most. The Portuguese dictatorship refused

57

to acknowledge or to cooperate in honouring them, as it would have exposed Salazar's duplicity.

What was rather surprising, according to the de Oliveira Evora journal entries and indeed from other sources, was that officials did not seem to realise that Jewish refugees were not seeking to stay in Portugal. What many of them did not know, or indeed seemed to care about, was that Portugal had Jewish citizens which increased when they fled Spain.

On both occasions, 1492 and 1939, Jews were welcomed in Portugal, by the Order of the Society of Jesus in Evora and Tomar. Therefore, by 1940 there existed a centuries-old vibrant Jewish community which played a significant role in the country. The business community supported by the Jesuits made regular representations to the government on behalf of refugees. These groups also raised funds so that 'these temporary visitors,' as described by Portuguese business groups, would receive better treatment. Available evidence from personal journals and local media show that in towns with established Jewish communities such as Evora, refugees received a range of support, predominantly accommodation and access to services in Lisbon where they had to remain until departure.

Despite being informed of these activities by business leaders in their regular meetings, Salazar did not overtly discourage his supporters from assisting refugees but simply said that he did not want to openly welcome Jewish refugees for reasons already known to these groups. Soon after one of these meetings in 1940, he stated, 'Portugal is a poor country and could not accommodate migrants as it could not afford to feed them or give them jobs.' The reality was different but compelling, judging from correspondence and journalists' articles.

These reports tell a different story. Salazar was regularly threatened by the increasing contingent of German officials in Lisbon. Declaring that his government must stop taking refugees. If continued to be ignored, it would have a detrimental effect on diplomatic relations between the two countries. Pressure even flowed down to the secret police. Knowing that they were poorly paid, German officials bribed them with 'gifts' which were products in short supply in wartime Lisbon. British embassy officials repeatedly reported the matter to Salazar and even made attempts to curtail these duplicitous activities themselves.

Into this maelstrom, poor Portuguese from the countryside were pouring into the city. Uncertainty and fear in these villages and especially in the mining towns forced the exodus. Finding jobs and making a better life for their families was now easier as the city which needed workers for its booming hospitality and entertainment industries. Lisbon was overwhelmed by the rapid influx of people from the countryside and the increasing inflow of refugees.

The result was a city bursting at the seams with rapidly deteriorating living conditions for the poor and uneducated. These desperately poor Portuguese people were taken advantage of by British and German spies, whether for prostitution or running errands, racketeering, collecting information and spying on refugees.

Hotels, cafes, and the casino became a hotbed of activity, predominantly at night which saw unwelcomed changes in the city. Unimpressed and frustrated with developments that he could not control Salazar again increased their numbers and bolstered the power of the secret police. They became known for meting out harsh punishment to those infringing laws and societal standards. Referred to as 'the thought police' by progressive members of the society, among them, leading business families, even though they strongly and openly professed to support Salazar.

In the 1920s and 1930s Portuguese elite families, like other Europeans, travelled, witnessed, and experienced the changes in other parts of Europe. Changes that had not yet reached Lisbon. Salazar, an avowed bachelor and an ascetic, however, did not travel outside Portugal and had no interest in doing so. He was undoubtedly aware that many refugees would have experienced the roaring twenties in Berlin and *Années follies* in Paris. By all accounts, he was determined to keep conservative Catholic Portugal 'unsoiled.' One presidential order, among the many, ordered the police to make 'every attempt to avoid interaction between local people and refugees,' stating 'he did not want young women's morals to be corrupted.'

Wealthy men, however, were not held to account. Living in well-heeled suburbs surrounding Lisbon, they were known to the police and administrative officials as advocates of Salazar and supported his policies which mostly benefited their businesses. Other men who were not exempted, simply bribed the poorly paid police. Those unable to pay spent time in prison skipping legal proceedings, and at the mercy of the secret police. Despite Salazar's continued protestations and increasing legislation, wealthy Portuguese men were unhampered in their nocturnal activities mixing freely with refugees and tourists.

Perched on the south bank of the river Tagus, where it meets the Atlantic Ocean, is Restelo, one of Lisbon's wealthiest suburbs. Well known for its geographic position, history and wealth, it also received greater acclaim and fame as a result of Portugal's greatest poet, Luiz Vaz do Camoes. In his 1572 epic poem, *Os Lusiadas*, (original name of Portugal), Camoes, decried the pessimism of the mythical old man of Restelo for having no faith in the navigators who were traversing the globe and opening the world for Portugal to build a great empire. It is indeed a poem of epic proportions read by every schoolchild and read to illiterate sailors on sailing ships simply to vilify the men of Restelo.

In an ancient *Mansao* (mansion) in Restelo, standing sentinel on the steep side of a hill with a half-merged prow of a seventeenth-century boat lived a man who Camoes was not prescient to know would contradict his pessimism. The boat guarding the belle epoch saved the life of his great grandfather when he was exploring the rocky outcrop of the Madeira islands. With ancestors, steeped in the history of the Empire, he had also participated in voyages in sailing ships. Preserving the remnants of the boat was sacrosanct. Still being painted on its patina of centuries with colours of the Order of Christ tinged with hints of fading gold, the fragments of the ship remained a beacon from which in tempestuous times he would remonstrate and vociferously vilify Camoes.

Compounding it, with outstretched arms, wearing a stiff-collared white shirt and black coat, reaching to touch the sky, with his head thrown back, Dom Fernando de Oliveira Evora was known to invoke men to obey the will of God, shouting to heaven proudly quoting the Holy Scriptures. And just in case God had given up on him, he appealed to the Saints to come to the assistance of sailors traversing the globe. Continuing his tirade shouting: *'ouvir minha voz deus'* (hear my voice God.) Irritated, believing God may have given up on Portugal, he calmly cried *mi voz escuchuras valgame dios.* Interrupting this melodrama only to reach for his gold fob watch, fiddling with it: time after time.

A habit vicariously learnt from his grandfather, he checked that it synchronised with the chimes of the inherited wall clock. Each, and every morning, he prosecuted his ritual of setting the clocks with the six o'clock ringing of the church bells. Centuries-old but mandated on the peninsula was the belief in the persecuted Catholic, John Donne. 'For whom the tolls. It tolls for thee.' Believing the bells toll for him. Telling him to capture the rhythm of time, to set up his daily routine for meals to be on time and for visitors to arrive on time. With the outbreak of war, he was regularly questioned by Yolanda for his petulance. But little changed. He still set time and called on the Holy Trinity, stopping only to shout at Camoes, the poet, 'Oh heavens, I am here. We are all men of our time.'

Reporting on her *grande pia to* her *grande avo* was a child who witnessed and carefully observed the protestations, which increased as they grew older. Growing up in these surroundings, a child was suffused in the machinations and compelled to follow her grandmother's example. Sitting with her, each day, they confided in their journal. Mesmerised by her grandfather's eccentricities and rituals, which she sensed her grandmother was growing tired of, it piqued her curiosity. Encouraged by Yolanda, however, Olga Sara became the documentary maker. It was of two women having to contend with a distant old man, Presupposing, a creative young lady was inspired, developing a fertile imagination, nurtured by her grandmother. Traits she would come to imbue in her children.

Without a regular routine, and without wanting to be noticed by officials, in chosen isolation from the opprobrium of Salazar, Dom Fernando de Oliveira Evora, his wife Yolanda and granddaughter Lia Maria lived quietly in their mansion. Standing sentinel in the expansive entrance hall was an early flame mahogany case standing wall clock welcoming old seafarers and vestments, with its pendulum of gold in perpetual motion chiming them in and out looking down at the globe that once spun on its axis.

An all compromising wife, a picture of patience, waiting and observing but unaccustomed to commenting, just so that this old man could hold regular council with Bishops and Jesuits. There in that Belle Epoque, with rooms of volume, cluttered with an embarrassment of riches, a testimony of the de Oliveira Evora dynasty lived that old man true to the sea and Empire. A spectacle witnessed by women who wrote details of his petulance in their journals.

Served with coffee from Brazil and Portuguese pastry and tarts, baked by old Maria dos Santos and her kitchen maid, may have been what really drew the regular cavalcade of vestments. But by all accounts, the de Oliveira Evora family, with its history deeply interwoven with Empire and Church, observed their sacred obligations of donations, a homage to God and the Holy Trinity, hoping for absolution for sins they committed, and forgiveness for sins they will be committing.

In a mansion festooned with heirloom, standing pride of place were several instruments of navigation, a sextant, more decorative than it had been when in use during the voyage of discoveries. And in that era considered an ingenious invention. Now superseded, it was a navigational instrument measuring the angle between an astronomical object and the horizon.

Vigorously and frequently, Dom Fernando, without question would declare that by 1922 it had become an instrument for aeronautical navigation thanks to Portuguese naval officer Gago Coutinho. Proudly proclaiming it as another of the de Oliveira Evora's contributions: from 'sea to sky.' Imagine how the spirit of Dom Fernando would proudly proclaim it as the invention of his time. Similarly, acknowledging that pride of place was the astrolabe, an inheritance from his great grandfather.

In his cluttered study, he was surrounded by innumerable manifest and shipping reports piled in well-worn stacks, like the correspondence his ancestors exchanged with their business partners all over the Empire which to them meant the whole wide world. Old man Dom Fernando regularly peered into yesteryear's binoculars aligned with the estuary of the Tagus. As age wearied him, he often imagined misadventure at sea, loudly shouting instructions that were silent to the new navigators, because he was still only accounting for ships sailing with the wind.

Undaunted and uninterrupted, he regularly recalled tales of ships emblazoned with sails with the Order of Christ entering the Tagus, carrying cargo different, *je ne sais pas*, to those his family traded with for centuries. The longest river on the Iberian Peninsula, it was named by a Spanish king who declared its bed had sands of gold. Mountains of gold were not found in Spain and Portugal. During that period, it was pillaged from Latin America.

Every corner of that expansive Brazil wood-panelled study was cluttered with maps of sea routes, rolled up and bound with faded ribbons, once remembered to be red. Now superseded but a relic of discoveries by his ancestors, as were the books stacked by category on every imaginable subject from the old and new world. Pride of place in his collection were books on the Church, Empire and navigators. Dom Fernando was a man privileged, belligerent and capricious.

Evidently, a witness in waiting for seventeen years to give testimony was his petite granddaughter, with slightly curly black hair, brown eyes and fair complexion imbued with an adventurous spirit. Lia Maria had progressed in her choice of studies in music at the Academy in Lisbon. Moved by her father to her grandparents' home, shortly after birth, according to her grandmother's journal: it was not for her to question. Her mother Maria Camargo de Oliveira Evora, struggled with pregnancy, remaining weak for several months after childbirth. Lia Maria's father decided that mother and daughter must stay with his parents where they would receive better care in Restelo, while he returned home to Evora, from where he managed the family's business conglomerate operating in Madeira and Brazil.

FOR EVORA FORTUNES

By the sixteenth century, the de Oliveira was already an old established landowning family originating from the Alentejo region in central southwest Portugal. Evora is the name of the region's city. Intermarriage was common between these old families and most had members who were Jesuits. Apparently, these factors contributed to the de Oliveira achieving prominence in the municipality, which led to the foray into trading with the Braganza nobility. A formidable partnership was consolidated with its commercial enterprise in Madeira.

Families who improved their social status through contribution to the Church and Monarchy and their municipality had bestowed on them the name of the town. Centuries later the family still bears the name: de Oliveira Evora. With support from the Braganza nobility, the Monarchy was petitioned with patronage and the de Oliveira Evora were inducted into the ranks of the minor nobility. Improving their status in the nobility was unquestionably a major factor in their endeavours to build the Empire.

The town of Evora was steeped in tradition from its history as the Roman capital of Portugal. Its architecture is incomparable to anywhere else on the Iberian Peninsula. A walled city, Evora comprises several town squares surrounded by mansions and replete with churches. Portuguese Nobel Laureate for literature, Jose Saramago's, seminal work was about his pilgrimage through Portugal in which he waxed lyrical about the beauty of Evora.

Exquisitely designed places include *Giraldo Praca* (square) with its magnificent Cathedral and ruins of the temple of Diana, hosts the thirteen-panel friezes of the life of the Virgin Mary. The work of Flemish painters, on display at the museum, have all been credited for contributing to making Evora an exceptionally beautiful Portuguese city. Evora Palace was also one of the most outstanding royal residences where renowned artists and intellectuals had audiences, as did a network of wealthy families, where it was easier to influence royalty away from prying eyes in Lisbon.

Occupied by Romans and then Moors of Islamic North Africa, Evora also had a sizeable Jewish community, which increased significantly after their expulsion from Spain. All these groups have been acknowledged as having contributed significantly to the city becoming one of the wealthiest and most important in Portugal. Evidence of the large Jewish community displayed in the exquisite multicoloured tiled houses in narrow cobblestone streets, easily demonstrate their contribution to all aspects of the city. There, however, was little evidence of Moors or indeed *Mouriscos,* Muslim converts to Christianity. Unlike Spain, Portugal was more determined to eradicate all traces of the Moors. Nevertheless, many places of significance built by Moors were modified to eradicate Islamic features and portray Christianity.

The Jewish community escaping Spanish marauders in the fifteenth century was reluctantly welcomed by the Portuguese, except for members of the Society of Jesus who openly welcomed and protected them. Impressed with the Jews, a Jesuit, Father Huarte wrote, *The Examination of Genius* and stated, 'The Jewish mind was better fitted for learning than that of any other.' Respect from the Jesuits was because both placed education high in their order of priority.

Jesuits, who were advisors to the Portuguese Monarchy, influenced their opinion on the Jewish community. Pointing out that they could be an asset because of their financial and commercial skills. It resulted in Jews being appointed to government administration such as in the Treasury. Jews were also active in trade and finance. Evidence of their financial activities remains in a street eponymous with money lenders and bankers for five centuries. Which allowed them to become a major contributor to the building of the Empire.

Although they lived in a few towns in Portugal, the Jewish community were all considered to be under a municipality which administered their civil and religious governance. It was headed by a rabbi appointed by the Monarch. The stature of the office was recognised by a coat of arms of Portugal with the words *'Chief Rabbi of Portugal.'* A rabbi had the same authority as a magistrate. Sentences delivered by him were under the authority of the Monarch and signed and stamped with the coat of arms.

The significance of the rabbi was evident as each town had an annual election to vote for its own rabbi. Jews were governed under Rabbinic and Portuguese laws. Additionally, influenced by the Jesuits and business families, laws were specifically designed for Jews. Treatment of Jews in Portugal was never consistent, but it was supposedly better than what they endured in Spain as has been clearly documented. Yet both were Catholic countries.

The Jewish community in Evora bore a similarity to those in Lisbon and Oporto. They owned their synagogue, but in Evora paid higher taxes that other Portuguese citizens. Yet they were forced to live in prescribed areas, segregated from Christians by walls and gates. Designated areas were modelled after the municipal organisation under the authority of an official appointed by the king.

For occupations, they were merchants, bankers, financiers, and public officials. They were also men of science and some were highly respected physicians. The poorer Jews were skilled craftsmen, tailors, goldsmiths, and blacksmiths; forming an important group that influenced all aspects of Portuguese society. Incrementally they became a significant part of the economy too, which increased in partnership and with Catholic Establishment families.

Recognition for their contribution to the country, came when the Empire was at its zenith in the sixteenth and seventeenth centuries. It ushered in a period of unprecedented laxity. New laws were promulgated decreeing that Jews must not be subjected to extortion. Ordinary tax, like the rest of the citizens, was all that they had to pay. During this period, Jews moved from Braganza to Evora where they received more favourable treatment and admitted to it being a boon as they made more money than they ever did there. This influx brought a new period of development in Evora. Undoubtedly, it contributed to lifting the profile of Evora, which was known as 'the richest Portuguese city.'

An example of the respect Jews had achieved was demonstrated by Queen Catherine of Braganza. When she became ill, she requested that Dr Antonio Mendes, who was Jewish and a professor of medicine at Coimbra University, be appointed as her personal physician. During this period, the Jewish community enjoyed significant privileges and immunities. In return, they contributed significantly to the development of society by assisting in improving education. They introduced courses on philosophy and cosmology to the University of Coimbra's curriculum. Importantly they introduced the printing press to Portugal.

Despite the grudging acceptance of their contribution, which gave leeway for them to be accepted as Portuguese, Jews were still forced to convert to Christianity. Astonishingly, despite protests to the Church and Monarchy by the Establishment, the Inquisition was still held in the City of Evora. On trial were *Maranos,* Jews who converted to Christianity, but secretly practised Judaism.

To avoid the Inquisition and to demonstrate their commitment to the country and city many Jews also changed their name to Evora which was the name of Establishment Catholics. But most continued to practise Judaism in private. As opportunities opened for financing the development of the colonies, Jewish families capitalised on it with the hope that it will influence the government to allow them to openly practise their religion. In the early nineteenth century, King John VI granted Jews the freedom to settle and practise their religion anywhere in the Empire.

Lisbon led the way by acknowledging their contribution to Portugal in its period of scarcity. Finally, Jews were given the rights to purchase a property. To demonstrate the country's commitment, it was widely publicised when Isaac Goldsmid bought the prestigious estate of Antonio Palmeira. On the purchase of the estate, he was also recognised for his contribution to the country by being granted the title of Baron de Goldsmid. The Monarchy was ranking him with counterparts, honoured by other European countries such as Britain, where Nathaniel Rothschild was elevated to the House of Lords.

During this period of greater tolerance, intermarriage between Jewish and Catholic elite families received greater acceptance and recognition. The Rothschild were the wealthiest Jewish dynasty in the world, and they married into Christian families. Part of the European establishment, the Rothschild had links to Jews in Portugal and encouraged them to lend money to the government as it was a form of security. Moreover, a common expression was: 'once they owed you money, you owned them.'

Early in the establishment of a settlement in the colony of Brazil, Jews who had converted to Christianity moved there where they resumed practising their religion. They became a driving force in funding the development of the sugar cane plantations in Bahia. Jews who migrated from Evora or were converts married into the staunchly Catholic de Oliveira Evora family in Brazil. No evidence of this practice was discovered in Madeira which had a much smaller Jewish community. Like the de Oliveira Evora, some of these family members were Jesuits and others officers in the armed forces in Brazil.

A convention developed in elite Catholic families on the Iberian Peninsula and practised in Latin America when there are two sons, one must join a religious order and the other the military. There is evidence of this custom being carried out until the nineteenth century. The reason this practice waned was that as families had fewer children, men were needed in business, at a time when business was strictly a family enterprise.

All these traditions, practices and conventions were evident in the de Oliveira Evora dynasty throughout their establishments in the Empire, until the nineteenth century when commerce replaced the Church and the military. At that stage, they became patrons of both institutions in Portugal and Brazil as insurance of their dynasty. Dom Fernando de Oliveira Evora wanted to maintain these practices and inculcated his three sons to maintain the family tradition. His sons joined their expansive family business with its major bases in Evora, Lisbon, Madeira, and Sao Paulo.

Commencing with trading spices as the demand for pepper, cloves, ginger and nutmeg grew rapidly, made for a very profitable but risky business. As demand for spices in Europe increased, traders capitalised on relationships established with other families in Evora and Lisbon. They expanded both the commodities they traded and the countries they supplied. Capital was needed for expansion and business diversification.

Portugal's expansive network of trading posts was the harbinger for spreading its accounting system. They developed a financial model with Jewish financiers, which was a family secret. As their businesses spread out across the Empire, so did their financial and accounting model which was their first movers' advantage. Diversifying and large-scale agriculture to monopolise the industry became their strategic imperative. With the increasing demand for products in Europe, the shortage of manpower became a major limitation to growth and prosperity. No crop would come to epitomise this fact more than sugarcane. The Portuguese knew it was labour intensive as they planted it in Madeira, having taken the sugarcane from Sicily. Compared to Sicily, Madeira's climate and soil produced higher yields. In Brazil, however, sugar propelled the Empire to its zenith. Colonisers accelerated their rapacious behaviour ushering in a new phase of colonisation.

With its successful spice trading history, which had now become more competitive as the Dutch entered the market, the de Oliveira Evora family turned to investing in sugar plantations. Commencing with plantations in Madeira in partnership with Braganza, the families' partnership in sugar production was successful. Pressure for a rapid expansion increased as sugar changed European cuisine and taste buds. To satisfy the need to engage in large scale farming, the Portuguese established plantations in North-east Brazil and quickly enslaved indigenous tribes or Indians (Amerindians). It was hopelessly unsuccessful as these people did not have the physical strength or capacity to endure the demanding work. Amerindian men did not engage in physical labour. It was the work of women.

Enslaving Amerindians became problematic, as Jesuits protected them. Jesuits saw the native people as more amenable to other types of agriculture. They were indeed, and quickly adapted to growing maze and other agricultural products. Under the Jesuits, Amerindians contributed to the development of successful commercial enterprises for the benefit of Jesuits. Prevented by the Church and government from enslaving Amerindians, plantation owners sought to enslave labourers from Portuguese colonies in West Africa directly across the Atlantic from north-east Brazil.

Growing demand for labourers made slave trading a very profitable business as colonial powers, such as Britain cultivated sugar in the West Indies. Using slave labour,

Americans were increasing cotton productional in the Southern States. Therefore, demand peaked putting significant pressure on supply. This was resolved with shortening the time it took to transport people. Salvador on the Northeast Coast became the port where slaves were trafficked directly across the Atlantic from Angola, a Portuguese colony on the West Coast of Africa. Millions of slaves made the journey to the town which became the capital of Brazil for a short period.

Business peaked for the de Oliveira Evora which placed significant demand on their capital. Initially, money was borrowed from the Genovese who was funding much of the slave trade, but they were also competitors. As demand grew so did the cost of capital. The trading families were a close network that assisted each other. In Evora, Jews were the bankers and money lenders and generally worked in financial institutions. The Moses Levy and Co bank was predominantly owned by a Jewish family. But Jews were also senior officials in the Bank of Lusitania. They in effect 'controlled' the country's finance and economy.

Revelations about their financial support were traced to the relationship with Jewish financiers. Discovering that it was established in the seventeenth century with an introduction from a Jesuit family member, through an extended family network marriage to a *Marano*. A similar practice, and for the same reasons, developed between Jews who converted to Catholicism. The most prominent example was the Espirito Santo banking family. An example of an

Establishment family that intermarried with Jews. There-fore, the de Oliveira Evora and Braganza were not excep-tions, but they certainly had a record for over two centu-ries or more. Intermarriage consolidated these business partnerships, preserving dynasties and wealth. The Second World War contributed to the erosion of business partner-ships between Jews and Catholics in Portugal.

Given the historical business partnership, Catholic families were expected to be sympathetic to the plight of Jews escaping German persecution. And these families did indeed assist surreptitiously during the refugee crises in Lisbon while avoiding achieving prominence with their assistance, fearing being ostracised by Salazar's regime. Nevertheless, Dom Fernando de Oliveira Evora's assistance went beyond the accepted convention, as far as is known.

In the late nineteenth century when Dom Fernando joined the business, it was no longer just a trading company, but a diversified conglomerate. With the spice and slave trade no longer profitable and the latter illegal, the business had also become less geographically expansive focusing on Portugal, Madeira, and Brazil. By the time his three sons joined and then took over the business, its expansion and diversification had to adapt to technological change. Dom Jose, the eldest, remained in Evora managing the business in Portugal and included as it is a municipality of Portugal. Of his two younger brothers, Dom Pedro managed the business in Brazil, focusing on diversification and creating a conglomerate as a profit centre.

Dom Alfonso, the youngest, on the other hand, based himself in London. After marriage to Caroline Boucherett, the daughter of an industrialist and descendant from Huguenots - protestants who fled persecution from Catholic France in the seventeenth century. Their marriage caused a schism with his parents and older brother. With pride in her ancestry, Caroline would not convert to Catholicism and did not adopt her husband's family name. Incrementally, the family business was managed by Dom Jose and Dom Pedro which, was the intention of his father, from family journal and letters.

Interestingly, in Evora, away from Lisbon, increasingly, Dom Jose gave nodding platitudes to his father's opinion or advice. He and his brother Dom Pedro in Sao Paulo took charge as Brazil was where most of the lucrative opportunities were being developed. Madeira was in decline with few new opportunities, but they had an established brand in partnership with the Braganza nobility two centuries earlier. The sons continually sought opportunities in their empire-building, many they knew, their father would have not approved. Apparently, he still believed trading and maritime insurance were lucrative. In London, Dom Alfonso was the financier and had agreed with his father about insurance. His opinion undoubtedly based on profitable companies such as Lloyds and Jardine Flemings, as examples of successful London insurance houses with a focus on Hong Kong. Dom Alfonso was also a financier of the Boucherett businesses. Both families had established financing networks in common which included Rothschild and Warburg banking houses.

Meanwhile from Restelo, Dom Fernando had sporadic contact with his sons in Brazil and London. It was left to Dom Jose. With her husband, Yolanda Braganza de Oliveira Evora enjoyed a life of their making, paced to meet their lifestyle in the splendours of a baroque mansion. Commanding the living room was hers by choice. On the mantelpiece were figurines of ballet dancers gazing over her as she lent an ear to the demands of her husband and granddaughter, simultaneously listening to her desired classical music and persisting with her embroidery. Their home largely reflected the family's trading links through adornment with paintings of ancestors by minor Portuguese painters. It was more de Oliveira Evora than Braganza, without question. Yolanda clearly enhanced the mansion to portray her ancestral nobility.

Proudly displayed on the mantelpiece were photographs of de Oliveira Evora and Braganza ancestors. On guard on either side were photographs of members of the Order of Christ, dressed in full regalia but without weapons. On the right-hand wall paintings of the family jostled with reproductions of old masters. The tables were covered with photographs sitting on specially embroidered placed lace. Models of sailing ships and statues made of Portuguese marble and Brazilwood by craftsmen, both Portuguese and from the colonies, predominantly Goa, Madeira and Brazil, cluttered the busy room. In midst of these surroundings, they had settled comfortably into a life of gentility. Until they received news they had awaited, for years.

In Evora, Dom Jose's wife Maria was pregnant. The announcement of the first grandchild was greeted in the family with prayers and offerings to the Saints and Blessings from the Church in return. But the spiritual fervour of Restelo was not reflected in Evora resulting 'in deep concern,' by Yolanda and Maria's mother. According to the medical records, late in the seventh month, regular cramps and morning sickness confined Maria to bed on 'strict doctor's orders.' The matter was handed over to Dr Daniel Edelman who was the family's physician in Lisbon. He curtailed Maria's penchant for entertaining visitors at morning teas and ordered her to be confined to bed under a new routine and to be cared for by a nurse, with daily visits by nuns who offered prayers and communion from the Parish priest at their home chapel.

This was not uncommon as Jesuits deliberately courted wealthy families and encouraged the development of chapels in their homes. By the eighth month of pregnancy, Maria's health had not improved. Dr Edelman ordered that she be moved to Lisbon where he would be able to deliver better medical care. Provincial Portugal at the turn of the twentieth century was not conducive to the prescribed medical care. Maria requested to be with her parents in Setubal. It must be assumed and imagined that circumstances and family procrastination prolonged a decisive decision. Impatient, as he was known to be, Dom Jose decided that Maria must be moved to Restelo which was the preference of the physician.

Lia Maria de Oliveira Evora was born in Restelo on 17 December 1923. According to oral history and by deciphering records, with obfuscation of the language, it was a traumatic delivery, resulting in the child's stay being prolonged in Restelo. It took many months before the family would pronounce mother and daughter were not bonding. Maria could not fully embrace her only child who was regularly ill and later diagnosed as 'having convulsions' which disturbed family members, nuns and priests. Persistent attempts to bring mother and child together did not achieve the desired outcome. There was a superstition in rural Portugal of *crianca do diabo* (devil in a child,) which was a curse that afflicted babies. It was prescribed that mother and child be kept apart and for the child to be cared for by others in the family or nuns. Incidentally, the de Oliveira Evora and Braganza's had family members who had taken vows. Exorcism was recommended. It needed a priest who was specifically sanctioned by the Vatican.

Such a priest was not available in Evora. The drive between Evora and Lisbon on poorly maintained roads was a challenge for the grandparents of both families. Initially, Lia Maria, her mother and nurse travelled the seventy kilometres between Restelo and Evora each week for ritual prayers and blessings. With six months of medical care and holy rituals, a process of bringing mother and child together was instituted. But Maria's health had not improved and neither had her ability to bond with Lia Maria. During these visits and after several months Lia Maria became more dependent on her nurse and less on her mother. Surreptitiously, mother was incrementally rejecting her child, while being astutely observed by a grandmother and mother-in-law foreboding a sense of inevitability.

Regular discussions on the child's future became a feature of family life. At the Restelo mansion, it included a Jesuit priest and Franciscan nun who were both family members. Not uncommon for that era. Lia Maria's convulsions appeared to have frightened her mother but ceased by her second birthday. On the other hand, her mother's health had not improved and interest in her child waned despite every effort, such as more regular visits, and periods of mother and child bonding, which both grandmothers did not approve of. Visits effectively ceased when Lia Maria was about two and a half years old and care was handed over to a nanny.

Monthly ritual visits were not an option when Lia Maria started school at five. Considered disruptive for the child by nuns at the Franciscan Convent School and acquiesced to by the families of both parents. When her health improved, bonding did not, resulting in a torrent of emotional sympathy from the grandmothers. This situation would come to leave a deep emotional chasm between mother and daughter which would dim the light between them for the rest of their lives. By Lia Maria's seventh birthday, her mother's visits became irregular as she was regularly ill and chose to be cared for by nuns in Evora. Yolanda's prolific journal entries of this period stated, 'she did not notice her mother's absence.' After many false starts, Restelo was where Lia Maria would spend her childhood.

For her Restelo grandparents, the 'child was fragile and precious' and had to be protected and gently nurtured. Wrapped in Portuguese embroidery, Yolanda, in justification wrote, 'she was never out of our sight' apparently even when she was with a nanny or members of the extended family. For Lia Maria, her grandparents and church were her daily ritual. Therefore, it was not surprising that the child's scribblings and drawings were interpreted and imagined portraying 'angels in heavenly ascent on clouds of splendid colours sailing.' Undoubtedly, Lia Maria was a constant for her grandfather Dom Fernando, sitting on his knees, stories recited about his father and grandfather's visits to the colonies on sailing ships in dimming centuries, mesmerising her curiosity, spirited interest and inquiring mind. Decades later in other lands, she realised that the sugar-coated history left gaping holes in his personal experience of the slave trade.

About her grandmother, with child-like simplicity, she drew pictures annotated with '*Eu a minhaavo com todo o meu coraca,*' (I love my grandmother with all her heart.) And from her, she was imbued with a love of all things Portuguese, Imperial and nobility. Yolanda was an ardent proponent of Portugal's national tradition of embroidery Hosted in the decorous parlour was a regular group that waxed and waned in attendance of spirited God-abiding widows. Most had lost husbands at sea or in the colonies. Their artistically designed embroidery became their act of benevolence. The fruits of their labour were shipped to the growing need of the poor in the colonies. Their sterling effort never satiated the need but satisfied their spirit, as they believed they were doing God's work. Enthralled and influenced by these ladies, Lia Maria wrote stories, drew designs in her journals and pressed tiny embroidered fragments between the pages of her scrapbook with flowers she picked from her garden.

Prolific with embroidery and jewellery collection, which were her avowed passion, to be later testified by her endowment of a large collection of filigree jewellery, that was indeed gold. These adornments were amassed over centuries and handed down by Braganza and de Oliveira and de Oliveira Evora women on special family occasions. Inheriting filigree jewellery over the years, gave her grandmother opportunities to tell Lia Maria of the splendour of their past and what each piece represented. Taking every opportunity to emphasise women's role in their design, working closely in the process with that old skilled Jewish artisan family who has been their jeweller for over one hundred and fifty years. Yolanda also told her granddaughter why her grandfather believed that no one, except him, could determine the destiny of the family and protect its honour.

Lia Maria received lessons from her grandmother which endured as she would also come to propagate them.

It included music of the great composers and the classics of English, French and Russian literature. Factors considered highly influential in Lia Maria choosing to attend the Lisbon school of music and dance. From where emotions transmuted, lingered, and pervaded the belle epoque.

Yolanda of Braganza went to Paris aged twelve with a chaperone to pursue ballet training. This was where she was exposed to the world and inculcated with the great classical composers and European literature, Tolstoy, Dostoyevsky, and Jane Austin, among others. She told her granddaughter, they 'influenced her life.' All enchanting, as they were to her granddaughter who would also come to pass them on for generations.

Yolanda was also an accomplished pianist. Her granddaughter enjoyed her playing, as she liked sitting next to her on the stool eager to touch the keyboard from an early age. As Dom Fernando grew older, he engaged less with Yolanda and her music. Curious Lia Maria would increasingly become the 'centre of her life,' as she recounted in her journals telling of her desire that her granddaughter would 'carry on what she was not allowed to do.' Reading these pages decades later, it invoked the emotional turmoil Lai Maria was experiencing as she thought of her grandmother, writing of 'her utmost integrity.' With emotional empathy, it would 'break my heart and led to my soul searching.'

Introducing her granddaughter to ballet at six, Yolanda dressed her in tutu and pointe shoes demonstrating the plie and the pirouette. Teaching Lia Maria that her posture must always be regal like a prima ballerina. 'With ballet, you learn discipline and posture. Draw your rib cage in, pull your shoulder blades down and extend your arms, like two beautiful wings reaching into infinity, with neck held high like a swan. You must always pay attention to your image, as to how you present yourself is important. It is how people will judge you. Remember to always conduct yourself with dignity and grace.'

Most importantly, 'always make your grandfather proud of you and never let your family down.' All these lessons Lia Maria never forgot and did her utmost to follow. It did come to be passed down for generations. Passing down these lessons, decades later to her children, Olga Sara appeared to be reflecting from the memories through her mother from her grandmother's Russian ballet teacher in Paris, of a strict but enviable position which Yolanda openly acknowledged in her journal. When writing about dancing her favourite ballet, Igor Stravinsky's, The Rite of Spring, she must have been immersed in it for its affinity with many aspects of her life.

When Yolanda told her sixteen-year-old granddaughter her story, the poignancy was tangible, as Lia Maria would write secretly, because she repeatedly sighed in resignation. It was assumed because ballet ended when her mother fell ill. She was obligated to return home. Her older sister stayed in the convent where they were schooled and became a Franciscan nun and was sent to Madeira. Who best to inculcate its inhabitants with Braganza spirit and love of her ancestral home? Her brother joined the Jesuits. In these circumstances, Yolanda believed that the responsibility was hers, as unlike her brother and sister, she 'made no sacrifices for God and the Church.' She must now make it for her family. Generations of her descendants who knew her story wept silently at her abnegation.

An older Yolanda resigned and sacrificed herself to follow tradition. But she resolved to never give up Ballet. In fact, she avidly supported the Portuguese National Company and the Conservatory and was acknowledged as a 'doyen of the era.' Seldom missing a performance and although her granddaughter did not pursue ballet, Lia Maria certainly enjoyed the performances she attended with her grandmother as Yolanda explained all aspects of the performance to the teenager who had already determined that her future would be in music. Simply because her grandmother encouraged her to subscribe to one of Bach's dictum, 'music stirs the emotions.'

She was certainly being taught to be God-fearing, evident from her spirituality and devotion to the Church. Emulating her grandmother, saying the rosary three times a day, as was expected, but the practise would incrementally decrease with her great-granddaughter to once a week and miraculously evaporated in the mist with her descendants.

To this day all members of the de Oliveira Evora Braganza families have rosaries with a crucifix made of filigree gold, made by Hagar Cohen of Evora and blessed at Fatima. When they make an obligatory visit. Ritually acquiring items of memorabilia to remember their ancestors. And then there was Yolanda's love of her garden of a multiplicity of colours. Another passion that would also reverberate and perpetuate through generations and far away from Restelo. Indeed, all the traditions she imbued and portrayed reverberated with the de Oliveira Evora Braganza for generations.

REFUGEES SEEKING NEUTRALITY

When the Second World war broke out on the 1 September 1939, Dom Fernando and Yolanda contemplated moving to Evora. Portugal, they believed, as did their friends, would have to enter the war because of treaty obligations to the United Kingdom. Lia Maria at sixteen was reluctant to leave her school and friends. Moving to Evora where she was an infrequent visitor and where she did not have any friends was not appealing. Influenced by her granddaughter, Yolanda persuaded her husband that they should wait until the government declared its intentions, which Salazar fortuitously did, and Dom Fernando may have had an inkling of, from increasing visits to the Gentleman's Club during these times of uncertainty.

To demonstrate Portugal's confidence in its publicly declared position of neutrality, Lisbon hosted the Great Exhibition in 1940 to celebrate eight hundred years of Portugal as a nation-state. A decade of planning and preparations had predicted a guaranteed flood of international visitors. But as the war intensified, this did not eventuate. Rather, visitors decreased as refugees increased. Salazar was exasperated and indignant as the policy of not letting

Jews into Portugal was not being adhered to, blaming them for besmirching the country.

The person held responsible for not observing Salazar's rules was the Portuguese Consul in Bordeaux, France, Aristides de Souza Mendes. He inadvertently became the most powerful diplomat in France as Bordeaux replaced Paris as the country's capital. The consulate refused to discriminate and granted all refugees entry to Portugal, which led to diplomatic representations from Spain where they had to pass through to reach Portugal.

De Souza Mendes argued that 'if they could not leave, they will be sent to concentration camps,' demonstrating that the Nazi's policy was widely known early in the war. Accused of disobeying the President, the consul was recalled to Lisbon and summarily dismissed. Dom De Souza Mendes later died in poverty. Salazar showed no remorse. Many years later these diplomats were recognised for their deeds by Israel. But never by Portugal.

Refugees were entering a city rebuilt and modernised after the country's most destructive earthquake in 1755. The rebuilding of Lisbon into a global metropolis was credited to the Marquis of Pombal. It led to his statue dominating the skyline of Lisbon in the Marquess of Pombal Square. Certainly, some sections of the city were booming and overcrowded. The experience in central Lisbon, however, was different. Wide and spacious, Avenida Liberdade gave Lisboetas the privilege to promenade through Rossio, which is the Main Square. It was all carefully planned for locals to stroll in the Praca do Comerico, bounded on three sides with government buildings and the other offering magnificent views of the river Tagus and the countryside beyond.

Lisbon also became known for its café lifestyle, which was indeed a major attraction for Lisboetas and visitors as the city's outskirts were run down and dangerous for outsiders. The pastelarias, credited for the best Portuguese custard tart, catered for and frequented by wealthy ladies as they were generally not allowed in cafes frequented by men who spent their time drinking endless cups of coffee, reading newspapers and meeting prostitutes.

During the refugee crisis, as it was popularly referred to, Dom Fernando made it his daily duty to explain the situation to Yolanda and Lia Maria, with his granddaughter the focus of his consternation. Well connected, he received information regularly from government and Church and officials at the Gentleman Club, and the newspapers and local and foreign journalists. Being informed was his avowed duty to meet obligations to his family and network making his interest in the situation multifaceted. With government officials, it was to be kept abreast of policies and to extend his overt support of neutrality. In business circles at the Club, where some members were Jewish, it was providing support, advocating and coordinating assistance for refugees.

At home, he firmly stipulated that his wife and granddaughter must obey his instructions on what to do and where to visit to ensure they were never exposed to the turmoil that was creeping down to Rossio from the Tagus. Of surprise, but suggested by his granddaughter, was Dom Fernando's instructions to his wife Yolanda to speak with the cook and maids as they lived in *Al Fama*, the oldest part of the city, known for poverty and violence, the latter endemic during the turmoil.

But disruption to any of the family's activities was highly unlikely. Most of the activity was predominantly in the vicinity of the port. After approximately two decades of relative quiescence, the port was again as hectic as it was during the days of the Empire which must have served to awaken Dom Fernando's interest, as he reminisced on his regular visits to witness maritime activity.

Now, once again, the port was operating daily on a twenty-four-hour cycle, loading and unloading products from many parts of the world but especially agricultural products and building material from Brazil and Madeira. And again, it was witness to the plight of desperate people, except unlike previously, they were not being trafficked. Refugees, however, were embarking of their own free will. Oftentimes for an uncertain Atlantic crossing and unknown destinations. Though most were expecting to disembark in New York, North and South America, the uncertainty of the journey resulted in them landing at other ports.

Jewish organisations were permitted to operate in Lisbon to assist Portuguese officials who were not equipped, or indeed interested or capable of assisting refugees. One action, among the many these organisations took, was to connect refugees from the same country or religious sects. Children travelling alone were most vulnerable, which the organisations managed with alacrity and care. Young women travelling alone likewise received special attention as they were prone to prostitution to survive. Or in fact, used by Portuguese gangs working with the secret police to force them to obtain information and report anyone acting suspiciously. Generally, most refugees were vulnerable and therefore subjected to harassment by German agents and especially the Portuguese secret police, purported to be supportive of Nazi policy.

Wealthy refugees were better organised as they generally had relatives in New York or London and as a result were provided with assistance, Portuguese contact and money. The common currency was gold which most Jewish people had escaped with, as it was easier to carry and hide, but eagerly sought after by the police and people looking to steal from them, or blackmail them,

Jewish communities in Portugal assisted where possible, but there were also economically constrained, and they too faced an uncertain future. Those who could left for North and South America. These Portuguese Jews, or their communities, experienced the historical life cycle and inherently knew that beneath the façade lay a deep historical ambivalence to Jews which was playing out in other European countries.

A suspicion that Jews were not loyal to any country except Palestine, (Israel) were heightened and promulgated for many reasons. The belief that they exploited these countries for personal gain and not to the benefit of the country was prevalent in Europe. Myths such as Jews were always ready to leave and 'had a bag packed at the door' were self-serving for groups or individuals seeking to profit from promoting these misconceptions. But, indeed, some Jewish people did have bags packed in case Gestapo night brigades caught them, as they were rumoured to be searching Lisbon neighbourhoods.

There was undeniable evidence that these activities were more prevalent among low-level government officials who wanted to induce fear in desperately vulnerable people. It reverberated with families that had business relationships with Jewish communities in Evora and Oporto. It was not a propitious time for them to expose these scams, as they were also viewed as 'suspect' and knew that occupation by Germany would lead to them being deported, believing that the Portuguese government would not stand up to Germany on this matter as no other European country did. Portugal was more vulnerable than most. Spain was not an option. President Franco owed his hold on power to Hitler and Mussolini.

As the war progressed, it appears that most of the Jewish community were confident that Portuguese neutrality would prevail, so they openly assisted refugees. The de Oliveira Evora did as they were intertwined with the community. Openly appealing in desperation, requests were for anything they could provide to make the refugees short stay comfortable. All anticipated and desired a short stay in Portugal. Assistance with accommodation and financial support were most frequently requested. Pressure for help increased as refugees ended up staying longer than anticipated, as getting a place on a ship became more expensive. And as the war escalated risk to shipping in the Atlantic made voyages more precarious leading to a preference for air travel.

Passenger planes from Lisbon, however, were targeted with the success of the downing of a flight to England carrying Leslie Howard, a famous English actor with Jewish ancestry. The act was most certainly carried out by Germany. It was discovered after the war that they had intelligence that the British Prime Minister Winston Churchill was a passenger. It turned out that one of Howard's companion bore a passing resemblance to the prime minister. This incident was widely reported in the press. It only served to make refugees more concerned about their safety as they were already increasingly subjected to being attacked and robbed.

In desperation, refugees committed suicide, feeling trapped in Portugal where they may end up being sent back to their country of origin and certain death in concentration camps. The Portuguese media and Jewish organisations were receiving reports of the treatment of Jews in Germany and Austria which they knew would be extended to the rest of Europe. Compounding these fears, the police were generally not seen to be helping, but harassing refugees. It led to advice from aid agencies that refugees travel in groups. Despite taking these measures, harassment by the regular and secret police and indeed local gangs continued unabated.

Overwhelmed by the task at hand, the Jewish organisations had to ration their resources while seeking assistance from their counterparts in other countries. With dwindling resources, priority had to be given to children, especially those travelling alone without parents or guardians as they were most vulnerable and were being subjected to exploitation. In those difficult times, young men were low priority making them almost invisible.

THE DESIRE OF ODESSA

Tascha Pietre Rostowsky was one of those young men. A nineteen-year-old university student, he was an Ashkenazic Jew from Odessa in Ukraine. Sitting on the western side of Russia, Odessa was a cosmopolitan city on the Black Sea. It was described as the Pearl of the South and was a city of sheer architectural and scenic beauty with its busy port, parks, and tree-lined boulevards.

It was also home to the largest population of Jews in Europe; renowned for its schools and synagogues contributing to the city recognised as a centre of excellence. Odessa was also a busy port where wheat grain from Ukraine's productive fertile land satisfied Europe's bakeries, especially French patisseries and Viennese cafes.

Like all port cities in the late nineteenth and early twentieth century, it harboured all the prevailing intrigues of spies and double agents. How much of these reports contributed to Ukraine becoming part of Imperial Russia mattered little, as its wealth was the driving force. Catherine the Great wanted to change Odessa. A marble statue stands centre stage to credit her vision for the city. Given her French proclivities, she appointed Duc de Richelieu governor. His French ancestry influenced the architecture of Odessa and a statue honouring him was also erected in recognition of his contribution to a city of marble arches and statutes.

After Germany invaded Poland in September 1939 there were rumours of an imminent invasion of Ukraine by Germans and Romanians. Advised by the rabbi, Tascha's father Sergi, smuggled him out of the city. As a merchant, who inherited the business from his ancestors, he was confident that with the family's global network of financers and grain traders, they would soon follow.

Sending him ahead, his parents and younger sister agreed that they should try and get to the United States. What rang through for him and reverberated on his journey was what his grandfather heard over his seven decades, 'Jews are inherently nomadic, and so have no commitment to any country,' as he was tossed and turned on his way in a cargo of wheat being shipped to Marseille, France.

Like most Jewish families of substance, Tascha was multilingual. Fluency in languages was a hallmark of the social status of a family. In Moscow he learnt French, a language the Russian imperial family spoke. He also spoke Russian and English. The family believed that Tascha was well prepared to make his way to France alone, equipped with gold to facilitate his journey and with a list of contacts. It was said that for Jews everything came down to gold for which the Portuguese also historically had a penchant. Before departure, the family committed to meet at the Empire State Building in Manhattan, then the world's tallest skyscraper. Tascha was leaving Ukrainian's gothic and marble architecture for a modern city sprinkled with skyscrapers, which he intended to help populate with more skyscrapers, even though the architecture of Odessa influenced his choice of profession.

A turbulent and fear-filled journey landed him at Lisbon railway station. From the aid agency records, they facilitated his journey to Evora to meet a family the rabbi in Odessa recommended. Arriving to find they had left for Brazil at the outbreak of the war. Reportedly, the agency also gave him another option in case he was not fortunate with his first contact. The other option turned out to be the Cohen family, jeweller for the de Oliveira Evora for centuries and highly likely a financer of their empire-building business. Serendipity indeed for Tascha, as he was told by his father that they should go to South America from where it would be easier to make their way to the United States. He held a deep desire, shared by his fellow travellers, to start a new life far away from Europe and persecution. A mantra they chanted and of which they dreamed.

Dom Fernando and his son Dom Jose had been in readiness to assist, so facilitating Tascha's, or another refugee's passage to Brazil, was a fait accompli. Purportedly, they had already assisted some refugees so presumably, they would have taken this request in their stride. What they were not to know was that assisting this young man would leave an indelible impact on their family's history.

With little time to get to know him, they agreed that Madeira was currently the best option as one of their ships sailed fortnightly to Funchal. From there it was easier to board another ship to Brazil. Tascha learnt that these ships did not carry passengers but cargo, which must be imagined as a *déjà vu*. Therefore, he would have had to be registered as a crewman making it easier for him to evade detection.

Avoiding official sanction, he was to travel under a pseudonym, which was not unusual. In the meantime, he stayed at the de Oliveira Evora's home at Estoril, a beach resort, frequented by wealthy refugees, given its propinquity to Lisbon. But also, refugees were less subjected to harassment by the authorities or hoodlums. Wealthy refugees also paid officials for protection. Close to Lisbon, Estoril had always been a popular beach resort, but now a novelty for refugees for the freedom it allowed them. It was a pleasant escape from boredom and uncertainty that overwhelmed most refugees feeling unwelcome and stuck in a place most were eager to get out of as quickly as possible.

The unseasonal warmth of the early 1940 Spring resulted in a congested Lisbon. Most who could went to places such as *Sintra*. Easily accessible to Lisbon, located in the cool pine-covered hills of the *Sierra de Sintra*; it was where royal families built exquisite castles to escape Lisbon's summers. Lia Maria and her friends were also used to spending summers at *Sintra*. With its narrow cobblestone congested streets, day excursions and weekends at the beach at Estoril became more appealing to teenagers. Given its distance from Lisbon, day trips were allowed, but teenagers must profess obedience to adhere to their families' curfew: to be home for the Sunday evening meal which was an ecclesiastical ritual for Catholic families observed for centuries, to be convenient for attendance at evening Mass.

On a day trip to the beach, Lia Maria's friends Lucinda and Olivia, all students of *Escola do Danca*, were chauffeured and chaperoned to the family residence in Estoril. They were told Tascha would accompany them to the beach. Perhaps, they thought Tascha would be their chaperone. After all, three young ladies without a chaperone would be violating all President Salazar's codes of morality. New ones were regularly issued to protect women.

Appearing aloof, shy, and nonchalant, with notebook and pencil in hand, Tascha quickly demonstrated his lack of interest to be with the young ladies when they arrived on the beach. Undoubtedly, a few hours with vivacious and noisy companions left him feeling uncomfortable with memories of his family and his seventeen-year-old sister Sara specifically. He soon left to sketch the hotel, according to Lia Maria's journal entry of that day and of that encounter.

The most popular venue in Estoril was the Grand Hotel Palacio. It was known as 'a playground' for European royalty, wealthy Portuguese, British and American tourists. During the war, however, it was described as harbouring a 'nest of spies', quite obviously predominantly German and British, always on the lookout for an opportunity to bribe anyone for information.

Refugees' uncertain status and vulnerability were exploited, sanctioned by officials contributing to antipathy to the country and its people. Presumably, Tascha was also of that ilk. Returning with a few refugees, they startled the young ladies, full of juvenile boisterous behaviour. Almost immediately, the young ladies announced they were leaving as the young men became excitably from what was imagined to be a rush of confidence, believed to be a result of over-indulgence in alcohol. Packing their bags to return to the house where the chauffeur was waiting. they agreed that they could not leave Tascha; accustomed as they were to strictly follow instructions.

Leaving the beach, the young men wanted to impress these young ladies so engaged in a playful tussle in which Tascha intervened as the fearful, tearful teenagers scampered up the dune to escape to the road. In the fracas the group scattered, and the two young men became verbally aggressive to Tascha. When the friends reached the road, he ran shouting, attracting attention, from local beachgoers, making the young ladies more fearful knowing the story would reach their families. The beach was busy as it was at a time when people were preparing to leave, drawn to the attractions of Lisbon's nightlife.

These young men's behaviour was clearly on account of their feelings of displacement and desperation. Vulnerable and uncertain, boredom and frustration may have led to their aggression. Causing harm was not their intention, but a result of a feeling of sheer hopelessness. Many refugees wandered the streets of Lisbon and were targeted and became prey to the police, subject to exploitation and racist vector. They did not want to stay in Portugal and for that matter, Europe, a result of what they knew and was experiencing. Getting as far away as possible was their only goal. Lisbon was not where they wanted to be. They all wanted to be in New York.

The increasing number of refugees arriving in Lisbon, however, contributed to the delay in departures leaving them to fend for themselves. Those with money or gold stayed in expensive hotels, mingling with Portuguese, British and German government officials all wanting something from them, promising assistance to get them on the few cruise ships. Passenger ships became infrequent as the war became more widespread. Unnoticed to the public and unreported was the infighting between Jewish officials and aid agencies with accusations of preferential treatment received by those of specific religious sects.

As a single young man, Tascha did not receive much attention. Preferential treatment was given to the numbers and families arriving from Germany and Austria. With hindsight it became obvious, but in 1940 to those fleeing other European countries, they were all in a terrifying quandary: ending up in concentration camps. A young man on his own with no family or contact, Tascha stayed at Estoril while Dom Jose explored every option to get him out of Lisbon. Meanwhile, unbeknown to her family, who would have vociferously forbidden her from meeting any refugee.

VIBERTO SELOCHAN

Lia Maria and Tascha cultivated a deep friendship, realising that they had much in common including communication, frivolously interchanging between English and French, to thwart eavesdroppers. Although they also enjoyed classical music and art, architecture became their obsession.

Tascha desperately wanted to repent his guilt for his behaviour on the beach. Lia Maria's dilemma was how to escape the cocoon of that belle epoch to listen to his confession. A cloistered life sheltered by elderly grandparents led to her welcoming any interest shown to her. New opportunities were what most people in Lisbon were experiencing. With interest in the refugee situation and curious to learn about Judaism, which her grandfather told her about, but did not explain, Lia Maria was probably more vulnerable than a refugee. When they were together, it was for Tascha a welcome relief from boredom and it allayed his fears and frustrations. And from Lia Maria's perspective, it was exciting, learning 'so many new things,' she wrote. Tascha exposed her to what she imagined 'was going to be an exciting New World.'

Apologising, he explained to Lia Maria the reasons for the incident. He requested to meet her friends. Neither of them knew that Lia Maria had regular assignations with Tascha, as she, on occasion, remembered her grandmother, 'you must remember to always think if people need to know before telling them anything.' Naïve from innocence, they met at Café Nicola at *Rossio* Square, sitting inside, as opposed to Café *Suica* nearby, which is outdoors. This

104

area with two famous cafes and shops was frequented by *Lisboetas.* It was time Tascha was introduced to her and Portugal's favourite pastry, *pasteis de nata (*custard tart.)

During their many assignations, the venues were interchangeable, but it was generally in the vicinity of the park, the river or the square with the statute of Pombal. All pleasing to Tascha as a reminder of Odessa because of its gothic architecture and bustling port. Unlike Lisbon, Odessa was a cosmopolitan city, which Lisbon was not yet.

Confirming her admiration for Tascha's intellectual curiosity, he told Lia Maria he was learning about Sephardic Jews who were from her country, Spain, and North Africa. Just imagine educating a young lady cloistered in a mansion on a hill. She politely promised to ask her grandfather as he knew more about Jewish culture as her family had been doing business with them all over the world for a long time. Which she knew for certain from her grandfather's stories. To discuss this would, however, reveal her meeting Tascha which she had to avoid as he was waiting for his voyage on the Atlantic. But to where was yet to be stipulated as the time and location constantly changed as news of the escalation of the war reached Lisbon.

Adjustments to shipping routes had to be made to minimise risk. Her journal entries for this period were prolific, as she was embarrassed at her lack of knowledge of her ancestral home which Tascha was educating her about. A recent visitor, she wrote, was better informed than her. Transfixed with his tutelage, she observed his delight in sharing knowledge and she was eager to learn from him without embarrassment. Lia Maria wrote that she was looking forward to what Tascha promised to write on his sea voyage. Speculating, she envisaged it would be about refugees and architecture.

From conversations over coffee and Portuguese tart, in crowded cafes, where they sought anonymity and strolling in parks, Lia Maria peppered Tascha with questions in the flush and flourish of intimacy which included his plans. Lia Maria's future was in music and Tascha's was uncertainty, but with aspirations to be an architect. Once declaring he wanted 'to create a new architecture for the modern world.' And for a better world for them. They talked about the architecture of Lisbon, Evora and Odessa, but Lia Maria could only listen, astonished with his invocation of optimism.

Waxing lyrical about the gothic and Manueline architecture as they strolled in *Rossio* Square, Tascha drew her attention to the exquisite lines and design of the railway station with its neo-Manueline façade and unique horseshoe entrances. Many of these places and buildings she had visited but never learnt much about. Reading her journal of 1940 from this distance, it is not surprising why she was enamoured with him. Interacting with someone who respected her ideas, which had never been sought, and was also willing to educate her to the world he had travelled and was currently experiencing. Just imagine the interaction that occurred between an educated European polyglot and a cloistered young lady from a different culture and religion. Yet with much in common that they never knew and did not have the opportunity to because of circumstances not of their choosing. Nevertheless, with determination, they maximised their time together.

Strolling along the river, they were intrigued with the Tower of Belem which she knew well, but never much considered, except briefly in history lessons, now wishing she had listened and learnt much more. Tascha described the tower as a classic representation of Manueline style to differentiate its architecture from the railway station. Lia Maria took it for granted, as these were old buildings that had been there for centuries.

Belem had indeed been there since the sixteenth century as part of the defence system at the mouth of the Tagus, and, also to commemorate the era of 'Discoveries.' In one of the tower's balconies, a sail emblazoned with a Red Cross was placed in acknowledgement of the role the Order of Christ played in the Portuguese Empire. 'To know history was important for humanity to make progress,' which the student of architecture scribbled at the back of the sketch of Belem, preserved in the bundle of a refugee's interpretation of Lisbon's proliferation of public monuments.

Perhaps his reasoning for waxing lyrical about Lisbon was because of its similarities to the seaport and architecture of Odessa. Reminiscing in the silence of a home and family. Communication was almost non-existent except the letters he wrote that the aid agencies smuggled to them. Tascha was passionate about architecture as, having observed the architecture of Lisbon with a critical eye, he may have thought it timely and appropriate to do the same of his hometown.

For her he interpreted Odessa's mixture of architectural styles, saying 'it reflected the multiplicity of influences: from eastern Slavic, later Cossacks, intertwined with its western style from Poland and then from Russia when Ukraine was subsumed into imperial Russia. From which Lia Maria wrote, he said with pride, 'emerged a unique style.' Tascha pointed out that the Lisbon railway station had similarities to the Odessa National Theatre of Opera and Ballet. Which was built in a neo-Baroque style, with colonnades at the entrance in a horseshoe shape facing the sea. An eloquent and informed description delivered with a 'desire for Odessa' which would be fulfilled in their honour by their descendants.

Tascha's time in Lisbon was spent productively which increased, 'like a man on a mission,' approaching his departure. With sketchbook, a permanent accoutrement, he recorded his stay in Portugal, as he had done for every place he had ever visited. From Moscow to Marseilles. Through his drawings, he opened the world to Lia Maria. With her, and for her, he drew the Monument to the Discoveries as a farewell gift. They gazed at a building that had recently been built for the World Exhibition in the shape of a ship's prow, portraying the impression of a ship cutting through the waves. Lia Maria was proud to tell him she knew what it was as they have a prow of a sailing ship at Restelo.

It resonated with a boy from a seaport. So, he was keen to see it. Years later the sketch became a subject of contention, as perhaps the first and only one of the building by a Jewish refugee, when the building was pulled down.

In two architectural drawings, the architectural student poured his heart out unreservedly through teenager love. *A piece de resistance,* now framed and of sentimental value to the family, as it showed the full splendour of Cathedral Se. Originally a fortress built in the twelfth century in a Romanesque style, it was the burial place of St Andrew the patron Saint of Lisbon. Another that warranted comparison, because of its neoclassical architecture and origins, was the *Teatro National Dona Maria II.* Fronting the building were stakes used to burn unbelievers during the Inquisition. Symbolic, its role during that dark period in Catholicism was not discussed. Perhaps this young couple did not know that some subjected to this fate were Jewish Portuguese and indeed Catholic Portuguese. But they were all Portuguese.

Reciprocity became their *raison d'etre* blossoming their affection. Heartfelt, Lia Maria opened Portugal, its Empire, and her family's role. A well-informed young lady told a story which was an amalgamation of what she learnt at school and from her grandparents' tales, which enthusiastically animated, as she was, they told her using artefacts, memorabilia and paintings. Not as well informed about

Brazil, which she thought she knew much about as her uncle lived there. But she did assure Tascha that she would certainly know more when they meet there, as she would be visiting the country as the war would be over soon. He was interested and excited to learn more as he was anxiously awaiting his sea voyage to Brazil via Madeira. Vowing to meet, Lia Maria's directive was 'Sao Paulo.'

The Portuguese foreign ministry consul representatives in Europe and Madeira had regular disagreements with the government. Just as regularly, President Salazar intervened and prevailed by overriding decisions made on Portugal's democratic principles. Consuls were caught in the midst, witnessing the desperate plight of Jews trying to escape persecution. All Salazar, his ministers and secret police in Lisbon saw was the chaos there but not the desperate appeals. The troika was unmoved ordering that exit visas to not be approved.

Aware of this hard-line policy, and having witnessed the refugee situation in Lisbon, the governor of Madeira, Jose Nosolino, sent a strongly worded memorandum to the Ministry of the Interior and the police objecting to the government's policy of not permitting Jews to enter Madeira. The governor saw the opportunity for the economic development of the islands, increase industrialisation and tourism when the war ended. Nosolino travelled to Lisbon for a private meeting with Salazar thinking in a face to face meeting the president would be more sympathetic. Press reports were that the governor had received a 'sympathetic hearing.' Buoyant, landing in Funchal, Nosolino received a note from the police chief: 'Jews must not even be allowed to set foot on the island.'

Unaware, Lia Maria was delighted that Tascha had gone to Funchal. 'It is a place,' she once told him, she knew, as her relatives lived there, so they may meet there instead of Brazil. He reassured her he would like to go to Brazil. For him, the opportunity of simply being in a place far away from Odessa and Europe was what he most desired.

Although Odessa was his home, he was unsure when he would return though, he was not sure he wanted to, according to Lia Maria's journal. Moscow, where he spent a short time was his preference, but he needed to go where his family wanted so that they will all be together. Tascha had told her that the architecture of Odessa compounded with his studies in Moscow, inspired him to become an architect. Yet, 'New York,' he said, 'is where I would like to go to see the skyscrapers.' It was where his father had also wanted them to settle. In Lisbon, he would often express to Lia Maria his bewilderment about his parents and sister, declaring that he desperately wanted to hear from them and see them.

Lia Maria's life would change dramatically. Promenading days ended abruptly when Tascha unexpectedly departed for Madeira. Around the same time, Yolanda started to question Lia Maria about her frequent requests for money from her grandfather who unquestionably lavished gifts on her. To her grandmother, she reported it was because she was visiting cafes and parks with her friends and learning about refugees. Which, Yolanda reminded her, would not be to the liking of her family as the government had prohibited young ladies from 'mingling' with refugees, according to official pronouncement.

Coinciding with Tascha's departure, President Salazar issued yet another decree. This time it called on the police to curb the interaction between local young women, Jewish refugees, and other European visitors. It argued that interacting with these groups was influencing Portuguese culture through the introduction of Western European dress style and habits such as frequenting cafes. Demanding they be on the lookout for those drinking and smoking and frequenting night clubs and hotels. Portuguese women wore hats and gloves. Other European women did not. They wore French designer clothes which added glamour and elegance to their dress.

Young people were generally attracted to this new free lifestyle. Women no longer wanted to wear gloves and stockings. The dresses of other European women were looser and free flowing which undoubtedly influenced women in Lisbon. Dress, beach attire, and behaviour especially smoking and drinking on the beaches were a hot topic, so much so, that it was regularly reported and debated in the media and official circles. Lia Maria commented in her journal on the lecturing, not by her parents and grandmother, but her grandfather espousing the views of an ascetic president.

Issuing another spate of decrees, Salazar's penchant for and entrenched dictatorial tendencies became openly evident with each repressive policy. Reports in the press stated that it 'incensed' with the impact of refugees on society. Under consideration were other options to limit freedom, with the pretext that he was 'concerned about the political and socioeconomic impact on Portugal. Believing that it would 'disrupt the harmony of society.' The dictatorship was more concerned about the influence these educated professionals were having on politics which he believed would foment opposition to what was euphemistically called his: *Novo Estado* or New State.

Policies of the New State were promulgated to 'stamp out' potential opposition, commencing with instituting censorship and media control. It was exactly what the secret police requested from the president. Their constant call for restrictions led to them being accused by the media of 'policing Portuguese women's morals.' Cartoons in opposition groups lampooned it as, 'immoral police, policing morality.'

Unsurprisingly, these repressive policies had little if any impact on men. The rate of prostitution rose as poor Portuguese women from the countryside and refugees had to find means to survive in Lisbon where the cost of living kept rising. Wealthy Americans and wealthy refugees, especially those who were receiving financial support from relatives in New York, contributed significantly to the rise in the cost of living in the city.

Unannounced and unnoticed, except proudly by the de Oliveira Evora father and son, another Jewish refugee quietly slipped out of Lisbon. Around this time, Lia Maria's behaviour changed noticeably but inexplicably. Except for the fact that she now called less on her grandfather for pocket money, to which he had always been oblivious, as he did with requests from the Church. An astute woman, grandmother was more observant and cautious. She received a highly unusual visit from the music teacher at the *Escola de dance Conservatoria.*

Unprecedented as it was, she welcomed the report of her granddaughter being seen with a young man, coinciding with her being late for, or missing classes. The teacher advised that she may need to receive extra tuition. Yolanda considered the matter and told the teacher she would discuss it with Lia Maria's parents, who were shortly arriving to take her to *Sintra.* This annual holiday with her parents became a convention when Lia Maria turned twelve after which she seldom visited Evora, allegedly, on account of school commitments.

Cafes and hotels in *Sintra*, as in Estoril, and places close to Lisbon, had similar experiences. British and German agents mixed with tourists getting out of Lisbon and the surrounding suburbs to escape bustling Lisbon. Contributing to Lisbon bulging at its seams, was because refugees had to remain there for 'security reasons.' To cope with the sudden growth of the population, hotels were extended with new sections. Aggravated, *Sintrastians* were now witnessing and experiencing what Lisboetas were complaining about.

Owners of houses, however, capitalised on the situation and used creative methods to accommodate as many people as possible with scant regard for safety. Ignoring regulations, miscreants bribed officials to overlook all infringement of regulations on the pretext of the war and desperate refugees. Changes in *Sintra* were not to the family's liking. Surprisingly, this suited Lia Maria perfectly. Contrary to her interest in the street markets and visits to the exquisite medieval Castle built by the Moors, which drew her to the town. Her parents suggested she return with them to Evora but could not, as she needed to catch up with her music lessons, which the teacher had agreed to offer at home in Restoril.

Eagerly waiting, she bid farewell to Sintra, and her parents and returned to her comfortable home. There she could escape to solitude and conceal the emotional turmoil she was experiencing. Missing Tascha, she was uncertain when she would hear from him. But that was to be a certainty for her, as he promised to write when the ship docked at Funchal. Tascha wrote letters that did not get off the ship as the law preventing Jews landing in Funchal was strictly enforced. After all, Madeira was a municipality of Lisbon and therefore censorship could be strictly enforced there.

Lia Maria's performance at music and dance classes was impeded by her lethargy and general demeanour.

Suspending classes, she started preferring to spend more time in her bedroom reading her favourite books on travel, history of Portuguese sea voyages and English literature. Besieged with misgivings, Yolanda was increasingly concerned about the change in Lia Maria's behaviour, which her husband put down to worms.

Lashings of castor oil only made her more regular, making grandmother having to resort to the Apothecary. But concoctions of lotions and potions could not unwind the mound of wriggling worms bedevilling her swollen belly. Neither did Yolanda's gnashing of teeth nor her wailing. She was sure and she was indeed sure. Avoidance was her denial as facing the truth meant having to disrupt her husband's routine litanies to Saint Nicholas of Myra, and preoccupation and renunciation of the President's ill-conceived and unwarranted unannounced ruminations.

When the cook reported Lia Maria's changing food preferences and loss of appetite, the 'child's secret' was no longer interminable. A chorus of voices from home, school, and feminine intuition unanimously confirmed Yolanda's instincts. Confirmed but with trepidation, her agility of purpose took on an air that mirrored her artistic performance of a ballerina. Upholding traditional Portuguese customs, she consulted her husband who informed his son, confronting him and his wife with their reality. It was an era when pregnancy was still considered an 'illness.' But for a family steeped in religiosity and characterised by a bestowed chimeric legacy, the improbability of transgression was met with opprobrium.

Tormented by fear, Lia Maria plunged into the depths of desperation, nocturnal weeping in the silence of her solitude reverberated in two bedrooms of a house of many rooms. Not knowing her fate, in quiescence was imaging her family's emotional turbulence from which she was never to know certainty, only the revelation of perdition that was to befall her.

The fear of the wrath of God, through the burden of guilt in their religiosity, was commonly held by Catholics and Jews. As was the belief that Catholics inherited guilt from Jews. Repentance racked grandmother and granddaughter. Repenting, they subjected themselves to benediction with a regular sprinkling of Holy Water and prostrated themselves in front of the altar before dawn each morning, before the suspicious congregation arrive for Mass. Imagining that only a century earlier self-flagellation would have been prescribed to whip the devil out of the child for the sake of her soul.

Ordained by the Church and executed by the family, prostration ceased when grandmother swore to hearing squeaking from the burden on Lia Maria's slowly swelling belly, believing that the baby must be weeping in concert. Languishing in an unfathomable depth in spirituality, Yolanda may have been purposely conveying an illusion to alleviate her granddaughter's burden of tedium. But it did not of itself deliver absolution. Attaining peace with themselves was objectified by the paying of indulgences as penance to the Church absolving punishment. Instead, it became a defining moment in their lives as they both wept disconsolately.

Unaware of plans for her welfare, Lia Maria was only alerted to her parents visit to Restelo, when she heard a car in the driveway. Pulling back the lace curtain at her bedroom window, she witnessed her mother stepping out of the car as the chauffeur held open the door, as her father stepped forward to hold her hand. In fits of tears, Lia Maria slipped into her bed pulling the cover, embroidered by her grandmother's ladies' group, over her head as her Siamese cat Diana brought from Evora, scampered under the bed.

Knitted in the parlour, that bed cover was an accomplice in concealing whispers of her assignations with a tall, thin, moderately smartly dressed gentleman with a book in his hand. Purportedly, the descriptor of one of the widow's maids. Senhora Setubal's reluctance and apprehension in disclosing whispering among her maids was only divulged after rumours were already widespread. Innocently, Lia Maria did not believe that her activities were conspicuous to passers-by.

Impatiently waiting, imagining it to have been eternity, Lia Maria's mother entered her daughter's cluttered cocoon, within what must have been a matter of an hour, before she sat on the bed. Taking her daughter's hand and in a tight embrace, tears flowed uninterrupted with them gently rocking from side to side. Stirring Diana, the cat from her nap, she jumped on the bed seeking to be part of the warmth emitting from mother and daughter as the cat had never felt. Feline frivolity induced levity.

For mother and daughter, it was to bring a lifetime of years in the wilderness to an end. That evening the extended family had dinner in solemnity, but observed the rituals, inviting the Jesuit to say, Grace. Even with religious observances, Lia Maria's appetite could not be seduced by the splendid display of her favourite dishes lovingly prepared for her by her kitchen, where she would generally while away hours in *falando* mingled with *cantando*. For the first time, bringing compliant cooks' and maids' disapproval and disappointed at the unrequited love of the dishes cooked especially for her 'absolute favourite,' *Cozido a Portuhesa* and dessert of *pastel do nata.'*

Sheepishly trying to hold back tears remorseful for unintentionally causing her family's distress, Lia Maria excused herself to prepare for bed as soon as the Jesuit said 'Amen,' after the novena, leaving her parents, grandparents, and clergy to hold council. Occasionally she would hear fragments of conversation that seeped up the stairway as inaudible murmur slithering through the spaces around the closed door. Locked away in her bedroom in a labyrinth of disappointment, with intermittent copious flows of tears, waiting in despair, she imagined or dreamt that shadows were apparition in their ancestral home, beset as she now was. Waking with the warmth of the cat giving her the comfort to sleep until eternity.

In fact, within a week, activity fervently echoed in a

house of silence interrupted by whispers that infiltrated hallways. With trepidation, Lia Maria confined herself to prepare for repercussions. The atmosphere of her home and regularity of visitors were invoking images of purgatory, where, according to Catholic doctrine, souls destined for heaven had to serve a period of purification before being allowed into heaven.

Inured to reality, she was counselled by the priest and nuns, but as grandmother told her, they had experienced these situations and are well placed to advise: 'she must listen to them.' There was not much else for her to confess as she had already confessed and accepted her penance from Father Xavier to prostrate daily in front of the altar and say the rosary three times a day in repentance for redemption. God's forgiveness gave her father Dom Jose the pretext for advocating a lifetime of commitment and service to the Church, as a novice after the birth of her baby. And for the child to be sent for adoption in Sao Paulo.

Turmoil ensued. Evidence of perennial wrangling between the de Oliveira Evora and Braganza families dating to the settling of Madeira resulted from de Oliveira Evora coterie vociferously objecting to the increasing role of the British on the island. Yolanda of Braganza had no interest in old animosity. Rather, she vehemently opposed her son's proposition and forestalled his plans. Dom Fernando's obsession was not the president's prohibitions but over the impact of the pregnancy between his granddaughter and a Jewish refugee. Foreseeing disruption with business relationships, and reverberation with government officials, where it would become a talking point at the Gentleman Club. Neither seemed to have resonated with any of these groups. It was perhaps because of the alacrity of action.

Redolent of history, the Braganza family again prevailed on this occasion which determined the destiny of mother and child. Reminiscent of the de Oliveira Evora and Braganza placation of disagreements from lessons with their business experiences in Madeira. Lia Maria never knew, but her grandchildren would, while unlocking their mother's secret. Loving her to the depth of despair, Yolanda was haunted by nostalgia accepting responsibility for her granddaughter's predicament. Spiritual penance cloaked her in black with daily liturgical acts without prognostication until there was a divine apparition

At seventeen, Lia Maria was cognisant of the repercussion, trusted her family and the Church. It was decided she would be escorted to Funchal by a nun and stay at the Franciscan convent where her great aunt was teaching. Since receiving her Holy Orders in the Cathedral at Braganza, Sister Francis moved to Lisbon and then to Funchal where, apart from teaching, she also managed the care of the orphans. These children were predominantly from Portugal. They were more likely to be sent to Brazil rather than be returned to Portugal. This policy of sending Portuguese orphans to Brazil to maintain the European population had been practised for centuries.

MADEIRA OF BEGINNINGS

Praised for its natural beauty by early settlers, and later earning the title as the Pearl or Garden of the Atlantic, the uninhabited island was populated with Portuguese in the sixteenth century. Evidence of human habitation on the islands were merely remnants from visits by Genovese sailors.

Commissioned by Henry the Navigator, Goncalves Zarco claimed Madeira and the surrounding islands for Portugal. Moving with alacrity to fend off competitors, especially Spain, Madeira was a Portuguese *tabula rasa*, in readiness for its history to be written. Beginning with the Master of the Order of Christ, Henry granted 'willing settlers' the rights to exploit the heavily forested islands.

Madeira is the main island of the group. Its mist-covered mountains, doves fluttering above the high steep jagged cliffs that plunge into the ocean lashed by Atlantic waves have over centuries created myths about the island's dangerously rugged coastline. The 'rock doves' perched there were supposedly the original species from which all the world's doves originated, according to Portuguese legend. Adding to the island's mystique was its natural beauty with its profusion of flora and fauna, like no other island in the Atlantic.

Exploitation and de-forestation were not considered

necessary for development. With exclusivity in perpetuity, the Order of Christ, following their tradition, wanted to develop the island as a commercial enterprise. Industries such as honey, wheat, and agricultural products along with timber, which was exported to Europe, made the island commercially successful which contributed to attracting avid interest from landowning families in Portugal.

Once the Jesuits turned the island into a thriving and industrious settlement, Portuguese nobility vied for control. Prince Henry resisted. At that stage of its development, Madeira was not like other colonies of the Empire, where the elites took control and ownership of the land, and peasants farmed it.

Soon after Henry died in 1460, however, the islands were granted to the Duke of Visy, a member of the Braganza nobility. Without hesitation, the duchy allotted parts of the island to a network of family and business associates including the de Oliveira Evora and Figueira. These families had a symbiotic relationship which was mutually congenial and consummated by familial ties. For example, the union of a former Franciscan nun from the Braganza nobility and a former Jesuit, a member of the de Oliveira Evora dynasty, consolidated a relationship which would endure for centuries. Networks, they knew, gained notoriety from failure. The Illuminati was a threat as it sought to operate far away from scrutiny, but it was not able to infiltrate a successful network of businesses. Working diligently and assiduously in quiescence, they ensured success and preserved the dynastic control of Madeira. Gaining kudos for building an impregnable well-organised network.

Nevertheless, the coterie remained suspicious of losing control, fervently working to keep the islands under Portuguese administration. The coterie was vindicated when they discovered the island was being considered as part of Catherine of Braganza's dowry for her marriage to Charles II of England. Cognisant of England's interest for a port in the Atlantic, the Queen Regent of Portugal was pressured by the Braganza nobility to ensure Madeira was not part of the dowry. The English monarchy did not overtly express objections when Madeira was not part of the wedding gift. Madeira, however, did surreptitiously come under British control on several occasions.

With the easy availability of water, productive soil and African slaves, sugar from Sicily was transplanted to Madeira and soon became the island's major export crop. Structured as a wholly owned conglomerate and controlled by a group of wealthy landowners, the trademark Madeira grew to become a household name in Europe and worldwide by the nineteenth century. Initially, the island had the largest sugar mills in the empire. But as demand for sugar increased, larger plantations and mills were required. A land-constrained island transferred its industry to a land occupying half a continent and plantations owners reaped significant benefit including unfettered access to land. Northeast Brazil's productivity quickly surpassed anything

Madeira could have grown and manufactured.

With the decreasing demand for sugar, as competitors such as the British established plantations in the West Indies, Madeira switched to producing wine which quickly became the island's major domestic and export product, resulting in the name Madeira becoming synonymous with wine. Surprisingly, the Portuguese cannot be credited for this achievement. Credit must be given to English and Scottish winemakers operating in Oporto, Portugal's second city, who changed the island industrially and influenced it linguistically.

Rapid industrialisation made the island a major asset and contributed significantly to the Portuguese economy, predominantly from exports to its colonies and the rest of Europe. With ships sailing between Asia, Africa and Europe, Madeira also became a major trading port, not only for spices but African slaves. Little evidence remains of them on the island as they were transferred to Brazil to work on sugar plantations.

Barely two decades later Europe was again at war. Between the two world wars, the islands were a major tourist resort and acclaimed as 'the playground for European royalty.' As a result, and due to Portugal's neutrality, the islands' capital, grew rapidly and became larger than many of the smaller towns in Portugal. Never classified as a colony, it was, however, incorporated as a municipality of Lisbon. Tourism continued during the war and grew with rationing in Europe. Madeira with its chain of prodigiously productive islands and natural endowments was avowedly self-sufficient.

At Restelo, Lia Maria's grandmother, Yolanda Braganza, had proudly educated her granddaughter about their ancestral home. Conveniently, the family agreed that she would give birth in Funchal. The decision appealed enormously to Lia Maria, as she anticipated Tascha was now safely there. Unquestionably accepting her family's decision, she assumed that they would have surely planned what was in her best interest.

It was convenient as apart from her great aunt, there were also members of the extended families to welcome her. The other pretext was as the war was escalating and there was uncertainty whether the Germans or the British would occupy Portugal to control the mines, they needed her to be in a safe place. That plan was clear, according to her journal, she and her baby would return when the war was over.

Dom Fernando who knew Madeira better than most of the family because of his frequent visits offered his grand-daughter advice and told her many stories, always emphasising the port, busy with ships from every country. Never did he neglect reminiscing on the beauty of the mountains and gardens. But then he could not, as in earshot was her grandmother who also waxed lyrical about her ancestral home. Yolanda went as far as declaring 'the gardens were more beautiful than those in Lisbon.' There are so many things for you to do and see, but you must keep a record of your activities, like all good captains, avers grandfather, as 'life will be like sailing in unchartered waters. You will have to read it to me when you return.' Lia Maria wrote daily and studiously, seemingly delighted to be far away from her family and friends. Even proclaiming her grandfather right. Funchal proved the ideal place to be, she boldly declared after only a few weeks.

On arrival at the port of Funchal in 1940, after an uneventful sea voyage, where she was confined to her cabin, reading and writing her journal, Lia Maria de Oliveira Evora was met at the port by a small party as directed by her grandparents. Welcomed by the warmth of late Spring, matched by the greetings of her great aunt and an extended family network, Lia Maria was overcome with emotion and gratitude, but wrote that she was distraught by the size of her baggage purportedly for a short stay. Little was any of them to know that the war would be conducted in the Atlantic, impacting on the islands, lasting five years.

Overwhelmed, the young lady was cloistered by nuns and widowed female relatives all seemed to her, older than her grandmother. In her discomfort of ignominy, to be the centre of attention was piercing her heart. An opportunity in discomfort to distract their attention, Lia Maria thought, was to draw their attention to the old seafarers' treasure chest, sitting pride of place, amid a mountain of luggage. The Brazilwood trunk, she told the family, was a special gift from her grandfather. That chest had already been sailed to Funchal. Whether it had ever left the sailing ship, no one spoke. She would never know but her grandchildren would set out to find its story.

Lia Maria proudly drew her great aunt's attention to the trunk declaring it was where she locked her many 'treasures,' which were parting gifts from her family. Nuns from an order that did not prize possessions, having sworn a vow to poverty overlooked their young charge's enthusiasm. Proceeding to detail her possessions, she told them her grandfather had reinforced the base of the chest with Portuguese cork, 'the best cork in the world.' Portugal was indeed the world's largest producer and exporter of cork, which was used, for among other purposes, but principally for wine and port bottles. The Braganza and de Oliveira Evora business partnership in Madeira imported cork and monopolised the Portuguese Empire market. That part of her family's story surprised her but was a lived experience of her family in Madeira. Only settlers drank wine in the vast Empire.

Resigned to a temporary period in the convent at Funchal with her great aunt, her care was placed in the hands of a novice, Isabella who was to prepare her for birth. A novice is a period of education before taking the vows to become a nun, which Lia Maria was saved from by her grandmother when she was fourteen. Similar in age, temperament and interests, Isabella was from Madeira. In her early period in Funchal, Lai Maria prodigiously documented life in her journal and letters, tracing the development of her friendship with 'Isabella of Madeira,' pouring her heart out, but also detailing her activities, including her musings and love for Tascha, remaining bewildered at his 'disappearance' and worrying about their future.

Encouraged by the nuns, she joined groups sketching delicately the wonders of flowers, people, and places, keeping her commitment to her grandparents. And just in case the description in her letters did not accurately portray the flowers, places, and relatives; they were sure to know. Lia Maria carefully contemplated what she wrote to her grandfather, wondering how much of what she was writing he would agree with since he did not seem 'to be taking well to change,' according to her grandmother's letters. Lia Maria was eager to convey to them that Funchal had indeed proven to be an ideal place for her too. It would come to encourage her curiosity, as it allowed her to explore and develop her creativity.

Isabella da Silva turned out to be a perfect companion too. Great aunt, Sister Francis was right when she asked Isabella to care for her. From Lia Maria's perspective, she seemed to always be right. Isabella taught her about all aspects of life in Madeira, though Lia Maria kept reminding her that she would be returning to Lisbon soon after the birth of her baby. Their friendship was reaffirmed and blossomed after the birth, although Isabella was no longer a novice, having decided not to take the vows.

Leaving the order established by Saint Francis of Assisi, which espoused a simple way of life and dedication to the service of others, was a difficult decision for Isabella. It was

Lia Maria's turn to support her which was also encouraged by her great aunt. It was cathartic for them. Lia Maria confession of her plans to undertake the training was stymied by Yolanda. In Lisbon and perhaps Portugal, nuns of this order were highly respected for their services in the empire. They welcomed Lia Maria presence as she was able to give them first-hand accounts of the situation in Lisbon. In isolation, the nuns now had a different perspective from the optimistic letters they received on the weekly supply ships from Lisbon.

Most of the nuns and novices came from and had families in rural Portugal, Poverty and a low level of education, had historically been a fertile recruiting ground for the Church. Lia Maria's account was, however, never detailed as she knew little of rural Portugal. Most of the nuns were trained in Lisbon but could not know of the changing face of Lisbon. Having grown up there, she was well-placed to tell them of the bustling city. She, however, would not tell them of breaking rules to promenade, participating in sketching monuments, and waiting at the port with a Jewish refugee. Temporarily tenured in convent life, Lia Maria offered to assist, which was initially not thought advisable. Perhaps she wanted to explore the life she was thwarted from and learn more about one she may still have to embrace.

Incrementally, her offer was incorporated into the school's program, when playing the piano her talents were recognised and utilised for the orphans before bedtime. Evening vespers and piano playing became a highlight for all, including the nuns as the Franciscans were not an order bound by strict rules and conventions, expect living in simplicity. A regular attendee to listen to her piano playing was the Mother Superior of St Francis Convent 'a kindly old nun.'

Lia Maria desperately sought private conversations with her great aunt as she knew her sister Yolanda would have given her all the details of her life and Tascha's. When they finally did, despite Sister Francis wanting to delay the discussion, she was 'absolutely devastated to learn of the Presidential decree which prohibited Tascha going ashore at Funchal. In an instant, it explained the absence of promised letters. Sister Francis said they thought he was likely to be in Brazil and her grandfather and father have been trying to find him as he would have disembarked in Rio de Janeiro. Uncertainty of her future was heightened yet again.

Lia Maria was not prepared for childbirth. Surrounded by nuns who were well-intentioned, caring, and kind, but she believed, with no practical knowledge. It was, however, soon an experience she forgot with the birth of her daughter. Olga Sara Maria de Oliveira Evora came into the world at Funchal Convent on 17th December 1940, surrounded by a doctor and nursing nuns. The priest stood waiting for the child to be prepared to greet her world in her mother's arms, blessing both and the baby separately. According to the Roman Catholic Church, the child was born with original sin.

Original sin is not a committed sin but rather a contracted sin. It is unlike other sins which are acts of our own and is a personal sin. It is a state of the soul representing the fallen nature that was handed to us by Adam who fell into death upon committing the original sin. It represents the fallen nature of humanity in which we find ourselves devoid of the original grace and holiness with which humanity was created (Genesis. 1:31).

After the birth, mother and child spent three months in the convent where the Franciscan sisters took special care of them and taught Lia Maria how to care for her baby. In this, the nuns had extensive experience. Graciously accepting unwanted children from single mothers or parents who could not care for a child on account of a host of factors which the nuns never questioned, as they just did God's work. Every child is a blessing according to the Church. To the nuns, mother and child were a special blessing. To assuage their conscience in perpetuity, the de Oliveira Evora had given an endowment to the convent for the education of orphans.

Olga Sara's childhood in Funchal was in propinquity to the cathedral of our Lady of the Assumption. Pristine, it was an oasis of calmness. Built in a Gothic style in the fifteenth century, it was dedicated by the Pope as the seat of the Archbishop of 'discovered lands.' Funchal lost this title when Portugal colonised Goa, an enclave in south-west India. In Funchal Cathedral hangs a processional sword from King Manuel the First. Religion dominated the islands' people who were deeply ingrained with rituals which became a significant part of their lives.

War escalated in Europe, North Africa and Asia and reverberated in Madeira resulting in great uncertainty. Travel was curtailed as ships and aircraft were prone to be attacked. 'A war baby,' induction into the faith could not be delayed by war. Lia Maria's child baptismal ceremony was performed by a priest, with nuns and extended family as godparents. Unusual but understandably in the circumstances, neither the child's grandparents nor father was in attendance. The former waiting out the war in Evora and the latter had still not been located but presumed to be in Brazil. Therefore, the family had to agree that without Tascha Rostowsky's presence and consent, the child would have to be given her mother's family name.

Lia Maria, however, did not want to deprive the child of a connection to her father just because he was absent, as she knew he would be there if he could. Therefore, she was determined that he be acknowledged against her family's wishes. A flurry of activity took place between Sister Francis of the Braganza family and her sister Yolanda de Oliveira Evora about this matter. The exchange of letters clearly showed the families' animosity towards Tascha, blaming him for his 'irresponsibility, disrespect of the family, and for being 'responsible' for their grandchild's predicament.

Supported by these two women, Lia Maria named her daughter Olga, honouring Tascha's Russian born mother, and Sara in recognition to his Ukrainian born, like himself, sister. Olga Sara Maria de Oliveira Evora were the names on the Portuguese birth and baptism certificates for a child of a Ukrainian Jewish father and Portuguese mother.

Olga Sara grew up steeped in Roman Catholicism. Judaism was not something she would ever encounter or learn about in Madeira despite her ancestry and the presence of Jews and a synagogue in Funchal. In Lisbon, the Jewish refugee situation had become a full-blown crisis which reverberated with officials in Madeira, and to a lesser extent with the inhabitants. Growing concern over the expansion of the war, people being displaced, and Europe's Jewish population forced into concentration camps, was not to alter Salazar's policy. Although it was an open secret, Lia Maria had no inkling of the horrors. A lone mother's desire, bringing up a child was for her 'to meet her father at the end of the war.' That is exactly what she confided in her journal. For her family in Restelo and Evora, it was a matter of contention for which she sought support from Sister Francis.

A series of disappointments clouded Lia Maria's life. Not to have had any member of her family present at the baptism of her daughter, was the harbinger for her clinging to spirituality. Baptism is an important sacrament in Catholicism and some other Christian denominations. Consecrated, when a child's head is sprinkled with holy water to free them from original sin and to welcome the soul into the Church. First Communion, however, is of special significance. it is an important milestone in a Catholic child's life. Being the first time, they receive the Holy Eucharist, which is a representation of the body of Christ. Only after completing this ritual does a person becomes a fully-fledged member of the Catholic Church. For its sanctity, Lia Maria decided that First Communion must be in Lisbon Cathedral where she took her blessings.

Soon after baptism, the mother and child moved from the convent, but not before the nuns and Mother Superior had confidence that Lia Maria had demonstrated compe-tence in caring for her baby. And even then, they were still visited by a nun twice a day. Many years later, Olga Sara, learning about her early years, with a hint of sarcasm, spec-ulated that the nuns had much at stake in the 'well-being' of herself and her mother. Sister Francis was next in line to become Mother Superior. Leaving nothing to chance, the de Oliveira Evora and Braganza families redolent with historical roots in the islands and contributors to the Church, prayed for a premonition for a Mother Superior in the family.

More likely than a Portuguese Pope, they believed, despite the family's contributions to the Order of Christ, with their 'best and brightest men' and centuries of offerings. It had been ominous in the secrecy of the cloistered chambers of the Vatican that a Jesuit must never be elected Pope. During the pre- and post-war era, there was only Sister Francis and her brother Father Jerome who still served the Church. Mired in controversy seven decades later, culminating in accusations of historical sexual abuse, the Church faced international opprobrium. With the first resignation of a Pope in the contemporary period. It took centuries and 265 popes, before a Latin American Jesuit, Jorge Mario Bergoglio, was given the insignia by the Conclave of Cardinals. Pope Francis was confirmed on 13 March 2013 to shepherd the flock into the twenty first Century.

In Funchal, the home of mother and daughter was part of the de Oliveira Evora privately held estate. Consisting of extended family residences, it was perfectly suited for the promised temporary residence of mother and child. An early Portuguese dwelling, it was contemporaneous with the Cathedral, more suited to seminarians and novices than families. Olga Sara remembered life in Madeira with great fondness in the care of her mother but tinted by sadness from waiting on her father.

Little could curtail her curiosity, even her mother's response: 'he was in the war,' did not satisfy her inquisitiveness which increased as she grew older. The war was her mother's stock standard answer. Festivities to celebrate the end of the war on 1 September 1945, a few months before the child's fifth birthday, was greeted with great expectations. Questions now arose about going to Restelo to be with her father and grandparents. Imagine a mother tormented with deceit because of a war that unexpectedly changed hers and millions of other lives.

Ominously, in August 1940, Hitler's 'Operation Felix' was to invade Gibraltar, a British entrepot linked to the Spanish mainland about one thousand kilometres from Madeira. But by January 1941 General Franco, the Spanish President, was reluctant to participate in the operation. Britain, nevertheless, invoked its treaty with Portugal and almost the entire population of Gibraltar was relocated to Madeira. It placed significant pressure on the island's resources, sealing its fate as a contentious issue between Britain and Portugal, producing a bilingual municipality of Portugal.

During this crisis, Lia Maria was recruited to help at the school given the influx of English-speaking children. Overwhelmed, the nuns needed all available volunteers and welcomed her interest to play the piano and indulge the children's artistic flair. Keeping the children occupied, allowed her creativity to transcend all obstacles. Teaching the children music and dance was her forte. Lia Maria's youthful vitality and exuberance was an advantage in facilitating other opportunities.

Invitation to become the youngest member of the cathedral was a privilege, as the *'senhoras'* who prepared the cathedral for mass, baptism, christening, marriages, and funerals were gatekeepers to the laity. Because of her artistic flair, she was given the task of selecting flowers for the Cathedral from Palheiro Gardens. A thrice-weekly activity, she relished, reciprocated, eventuating into a daily affair. Attracted there by the sheer beauty of nature, embellished by vegetation and a profusion of multicolour flowers, hovered over by birds and bees, exuding luxuriant fragrance untainted by the scent of burning candle wax or the smoke of incense. An enduring love of nature, roses, and the penchant to marvel at the creativity of gardeners pervade the lives of her descendants.

GARDEN OF LOVE AND LOSS

Established in 1801 by the First Count of Carvalhall, Dom Joao Esmeraldo, the sprawling and expansive Palheiro Estate became one of the most visited places of any island in the Atlantic. Built in the mountainous region commanding panoramic views, and a short distance from the second highest peak in Madeira, Palheiro gained international prominence after it was visited by Dom Carlos and Queen Dona Maria in 1901.

World-renowned for its 10,000 camellias it had a selection of plants from every country visited by Portuguese sailing ships. Calling into the port at Funchal, the ship's captain sought and generally received an invitation to the estate and in return brought gifts of plants to impress the Count and the dynasty that inherited the estate. By the late1940s the nobility were no longer owners. Continuing the tradition, however, the new owners, the Emest family, opened the estate to the public.

Lia Maria's enthusiasm and artistic flair encouraged attendance at the cathedral where, though she was viewed with suspicion by the elderly women, she earnt respect from the nuns who recommended her to the owners. Delighted with the offer of assistance, she became part of the team at the Palheiro mansion, which was being refurbished to cater for post-war tourism, with modern recreational facilities, guest accommodation, and a golf course. Olga Sara remembered her first visit to Palheiro Gardens mainly because of the 'happiness' she elicited from her mother and obviously as it would come to leave an indelible mark on her life.

Memories of perambulating in the gardens holding her mother's hand, compelled by her curiosity to keep swapping sides 'to see it all' was scribbled with a child's enthusiastic innocence. Olga Sara recalled that the gardeners always seemed happy with their work. The men stood up and tipped their hats and the women smiled and politely bowed. It was there at the age of six that Olga Sara decided on her future. And indeed, her future was determined. Looking up at her mother she confidently stated, 'I want a garden when I grow up.' She remembered her mother smiling as they kept walking, reluctant to interrupt the promenade of a splendid Spring.

One of the many reasons for the restoration of the mansion was for the ghost, many Madeirans profess to see there, to finally find a resting place. Wandering spirits will continue to do so until their soul found its resting place, according to folklore. Over centuries it had made for a good story as it scared young ladies such as Lia Maria and frightened little children such as Olga Sara. Superstition surrounded the place when it was apparently confirmed that a mysterious woman also haunts the chapel. Madeirans believed the ghostly apparition had been occurring for centuries and believed to have been a member of the Braganza dynasty.

Another superstition that persisted for centuries was a belief in the evil eye. Causing much consternation, a test was devised to judge its existence. The person had to put a drop of oil in a container of water. If the oil did not disperse then the person was not evil. If, however, the oil dispersed the person had to be given penance and received atonement from a priest. Here was a clear example that demonstrated how the Church adapted to local beliefs.

Surrounded by the chimes of tolling bells three times a day, before morning, midday, and evening services, guaranteed, according to belief, mother and daughter, as it did everyone on the cathedral's consecrated grounds supernatural protection. Once you repented for your sins, as they were told by the old lady wandering the grounds, regularly blessing herself. It was only accepted when verified by Sister Francis. That old lady as 'caretaker' of every place outside of the convent and ancestors' graves was called a witch by the children who believed that she flew on her broom. Frowned upon by the nuns, Olga Sara obeyed from fear.

Perpetually enmeshed in black, broom in hand, she must have been watching over, observing the child's innocence but perhaps sensed her fear in reticence, as her mother greeted the old lady with reverence, as did the nuns. For Olga Sara to be protected from evil, the old lady told her just before her first communion, to come close which instilled her with the fear of the simplicity of a child. But all she wanted was to put a silver amulet bearing the face of the Madonna around the child's neck. Mesmerised, she admitted wearing it until she left Funchal, and years later it was found in her treasure chest. That old soothsayer's omen about Lia Maria was prophetic as she turned out to be more of a clairvoyant.

Approaching seven years of age, a child must commence preparations for the first communion by learning the catechism. Olga Sara was looking forward to receiving special promised gifts of a prayer book and a rosary which was blessed at Fatima in Portugal, a tradition of the Evora and many families. In Catholicism, Fatima is one of the most important shrines in the world. Dedicated to Our Lady of the Rosary, as it was where her apparition was witnessed by three children from a family of shepherds. That rosary accompanied Olga Sara everywhere for the rest of her life.

Before receiving communion, her persistence with questions about her father, grandparents, and Portugal was related to her receiving the sacrament when all the family were obligated to be in attendance. Lia Maria advised by Sister Francis had been telling the child her father was in the war and they will see him when they return to Lisbon. She grew to abhor her duplicity for her canard of cowardice. She discussed her predicament with Isabella who, since leaving the convent, was working at Palheiro Gardens. They both thought at seven Olga Sara was at an age where she must be told the truth.

Lia Maria sought a solution to avoid confronting the matter directly with her daughter. Paralysed with fear, explaining the complexity of her conundrum would, she believed, be more traumatic than cathartic for them. Derived from a convulsion of creativity, her vision was so distinctive that it persisted for decades. Using the popular Encyclopedia Britannica with the assistance of priests and approval of her great aunt, Lia Maria devised a program of stupendous simplicity in 1947 Funchal.

Compellingly, reading about Odessa became one of Olga Sara's passions. She now frequently told her friends about her father's homeland. Though hesitant because of the complexity of its simplicity, Mother Superior came to support Lia Maria's, 'Magic Carpet Ride.' The lesson was camouflaged in playtime using that old map of the world familiar to the children. It probably had been stuck on the wall for many years, as it gave prominence to the Portuguese Empire.

Most orphans did not know anything about their parents, so the 'game' was for priests as the father to 'adopt' a child for the period of the game. The priests would tell stories about their real or imagined homeland. Olga Sara loved this activity, both for learning new stories and for the relationship she developed with Father Aloysius, 'who was a gentle and kind man.' She and the other children did indeed call the priests 'Father', as is the convention in Christianity, but she later wrote that it was with greater symbolism for her as she navigated her childhood and it can be imagined to be the same for many orphans. But with a mother, and her father supposedly in Portugal, she was most certainly not an orphan. Something she was so concerned about that she regularly sought confirmation from her mother, which she admitted to in later years and wrote about in her journal. Despite circumstances which were to befall her and the Church many years later, Olga Sara remembered Father Aloysius, with great affection, resulting in her sending her son to St Aloysius Jesuits School in New York.

For the magic carpet ride, the children would lie on their blankets on their tummy with chin propped in their hands, holding their head up high, in readiness to take flight. A priest would tell them a story of a country, not necessarily the country of his birth, as all were Portuguese. They would incrementally, and over weeks, tell children stories about their 'home.' Apparently, some priests used the opportunity to choose a country where they would most likely be sent on their next mission. The nuns taught the children in greater detail the geography of the country and its bonds of friendship with Portugal. They learnt Portugal's most important and most prominent relationship was with the United Kingdom.

Coincidentally, or perhaps Lia Maria developed it as she listened to a popular BBC World Service which was a lifeline for Madeirans in 1947. It was the year St Francis Convent School started the 'adopt a country' lesson. And it was the year European countries commenced their 'twinning' which became the 'Twin Cities' program. Its principal objective was to foster friendship and encourage greater understanding between people and facilitate commerce, a result of the devastation of the Second World War. Seventy-five years later it is still a successful global program.

Lia Maria and Isabella loved how the nuns made learning and geography so much fun that it became one of the children's favourite lessons. The nuns, seeing the children transfixed in fascination and how it developed their imagination, were overcome by emotions, accounted for by their tear-stained habits. Supplemented by real-life experiences like excursions to villages to learn about the islands. One of the established highlights was the warmth with which the children were received by the villagers. Visits always ended with much eating and traditional dancing. In return, the nuns sang with the children and the Church village choirs that sung in competitions in the Cathedral for many years.

These excursions helped the children develop their love of Madeira. So well known, they were featured in the media in the post-war years and even written about in books. Generally, they were mostly in praise of the Franciscan nuns as they fostered enduring respect in the community for their work with the orphans. It was also reported in Lisbon that the sisters were praised for 'the transformation they achieved' with these children. Isabella was one of those children. She left Palheiro and Madeira and became a teacher in Setubal in Portugal after marrying. She and Olga Sara continued a friendship with expectations, gleaned from their correspondence.

Lia Maria continued to assist the Franciscan Sisters from the Order of Santa Clara in Funchal and took children on many excursions to learn about plants and flowers of the world as it was possible to do at Palheiro. A popular place favoured by Olga Sara was *Mac Machico* where there was a camp where children spent their summer holidays. Perhaps because she had the opportunity to interact with other children, away from the cloistered reach of her mother. From there she developed a greater appreciation of the panoramic landscape and cliff face of the main island. Included was the vegetation of bougainvillaea and introduced eucalyptus trees which added to the island's natural beauty. These excursions were a joy to Olga Sara. It was where, with her mother, she was imbued with a love of nature and gardens as her great grandmother did in Restelo for her mother and she would for her children and grandchildren.

Full throttle, mother and daughter engaged in artistic activities with great gusto. Olga Sara recalled visits to the museum of the Sacred Art where the triptych was on display. History mandated it held a special place in the heart of Madeirans as it was shipped there from Bruges in Brussels in the height of the sugar trade. The central panel, measuring 6 foot by 4 foot, was painted by Gerard David of the Flemish School. It depicts the descent of Christ from the cross in the lushness of the Flemish countryside.

As a grown-up Olga Sara's love for Madeira was evident from regular expressions of happiness in her journals over the years. She waxed lyrical about her many summer fiestas. Most memorable was the annual September fishing expedition when boats carried a statue of the Virgin Mary to the chapel on the cliffs to give thanks for a successful year of fishing. Although she attended many feast days with her mother and the nuns, her favourite was The Feast of the Assumption of the Blessed Virgin and Our Lady of Fatima both of which were immensely popular with Madeirans.

Lia Maria occasionally played the organ at church. Though the liturgical music inspired her, it seemed to be for the high temple. So, she was instructed to focus on continuing playing the piano at school and as she did on special occasions for the orphans. They held a special place in her heart as she found it easy to empathise with them. Exploring musical styles was a speciality as she enjoyed their nervous laughter of approval. It is not certain when she became enthralled with the music of Camille Saint-Saëns, a French composer, who spent many summers on the islands and said it influenced his compositions. For Lia Maria, his greatest contribution was the harmonic sophistication of the music. Whatever the reason, Madeira adopted him.

Olga Sara was enthralled by her mother's easy piano playing style, which she aspired to achieve. Observing how music transfixed her daughter when she played, Lia Maria taught her to play the piano and taught her that to understand music you must first listen as 'a composition is a story and the composer cajoles the instruments to talk to each other. The real mystery of music is the composition, the creation of sounds, moods and rhythm.' Her mother wanted her to record it but had to spell some words, so she broke it into fragments to ensure the transcription was accurate. Those memorably impactful words written in a seven-year old's journal were expertly rewritten many years later in calligraphy, framed and sat on top of her great grandmother's Steinway which she inherited.

Olga Sara wrote that at that age she did not understand what it meant but did as a sixteen-year-old music student in Sao Paulo. Perhaps her mother had her reasons. How a mother sets out to deliberately influence her daughter's eclectic taste in music and literature can only be imagined from a long distance and geography. Lia Maria not only taught her daughter to play the piano but at an early age introduced her to the English classics which she would always read in English in keeping with her belief that authors are best read in their native tongue. Many Madeirans are bilingual as the English occupied the island for two hundred years before returning it to the Portuguese.

The short number of summers Olga Sara spent in Madeira was remembered with great fondness. Sitting with her mother on the cool blue patterned Portuguese tiled floor, common throughout the empire, was simply joyous. There was a custom of eating outdoors and for mother and daughter, it was in the garden. Despite its briefness, she somehow developed a penchant for eating outdoors and for tending beautiful gardens preferably where she could attend to them all year round. Lia Maria would tell her that *Lisboetas* did not have such a beautiful place. It was the reason they liked to visit Madeira. For Olga Sara what she learnt from these years would come to influence her throughout her life and be imparted to her descendants.

Unintentionally, it evoked a scintilla of sadness when she recalled that they did not have many visitors except priests and nuns and extended family. Therefore, the arrival of weekly, and later with greater frequency, letters from Lisbon became one of expected anticipated sensitivity for her mother.

Approaching the penultimate week of her sacrament of communion, Olga Sara expectantly anticipated good news witnessing a flurry of activity everywhere in Funchal. Knowing how important it was to recite her prayers 'by heart', she increased recitals of Our Father and Hail Marys and knelt longer than her mother at nightly prayers, to keep them safe from her premonition. But neither bore their soul. For Olga Sara, it was in anticipation of perfection when she would have to recite her prayers for her father and her grandparents. She imagined her father would be proud. A decade later she knew differently. Perhaps a Jewish father would be tolerant though.

Apart from school and Sunday school, most of her excursions were with her mother, visiting places such as 'Nuns Valley,' Grand Curral which was a place of pilgrimage. Despite her many excursions, Olga Sara never visited *Pico Ruivo*, or the Purple Peak, which is the highest elevation in Madeira. But they intended to on their next excursion to

Palheiro Gardens. It was not far away as the estate covered an extensive area. Olga Sara thought she may never see all of it before going to Portugal, but she never expressed those feelings to her mother, only confiding in her journal where she drew and described her fascination for Madeira's hummingbirds. Trying to understand why with briskly flapping wings these birds stood still, which was contrary to what she learnt at school. A mother devoted to her child provided the answer. 'Hummingbirds beaks suck honey from the flowers making the birds stronger to fly.' From that moment, Olga Sara promised to take her spoonful of honey every morning. In fact, that promise lasted a lifetime and for generations.

All these distractions and activities were avoidances but never curtailed her questions about her father now that she knew so much about Odessa, as she was eager to show him. Lia Maria had by then received information from her grandfather, that Tascha did not appear on the ship's manifest as recorded in Funchal. Dom Fernando surmised that perhaps it was because of the restrictions on Jews landing in Funchal, which shocked Lia Maria to '*para o amago do meu coracao*' (to the core of my heart.)

The assumption was that he would have stayed on board and possibly disembark in Rio de Janeiro, which she had already been told by Sister Francis. Neither her grandfather nor her father made attempts to investigate his whereabouts, which they could have through his son and brother, Dom Pedro in Sao Paulo. Perhaps, in keeping secrets, they did not want to expose him and his family to Lia Maria's predicament, as there was never any intention for mother and daughter to visit Brazil, despite what Lia Maria was led to believe growing up in Portugal. The complexities and turbulence in Brazil and Portugal's relationship were best left to men, her grandmother told her.

Mired in loss and emotional turmoil, she eulogised in her journal her love for Tascha and the life she envisaged for the three of them in Brazil, where there were no restrictions on Jews. As a twenty-four-year-old, her words were heart-wrenching every time her daughter would later come to read them. Her despair was eloquently expressed if somewhat disjointed by the invectives to the Portuguese authorities and her family. Olga Sara grew increasingly emotional when she had cause to talk about reading her mother's words. She must have held secrets like so many others over this matter, filtered like Chinese whispers. But neither mother nor daughter lacked imagination.

Despite being common knowledge in the family, it was not mentioned in Lia Maria parents' letters of indifference and irregularity. Neither was it by her grandmother who was a regular letter writer. In her correspondence, Yolanda wrote about renewal of Lisbon, Church activities, collecting new pieces of filigree gold jewellery, always reminding her granddaughter it was for her. Her embroidery group's new projects were lessening as the women were older and demand for their work lessened in the changing fashion. Most importantly for her was the seasonal changes in her

Restelo garden, which she occasionally reminded Lia Maria would be hers one day, as if either would forget.

Yolanda in her neatly cultivated handwriting never missed explaining the activity on the Tagus which kept Dom Fernando occupied, along with his stream of visitors with whom he shared the politics of Salazar with over Brazil coffee. Meanwhile, Lia Maria was still waiting on her father to arrange her return to Portugal, so that the child could meet her grandparents and great grandparents, which they eagerly awaited. Instead, Lia Maria and her great aunt Sister Francis simultaneously received letters that her parents would spend the summer of 1947 in Madeira.

In her journal she expressed the extremes of emotions she was experiencing and had sublimated to her commitment to her daughter. It appeared it was all in an effort, to protect her from any overt display as she tried to suppress her ambivalence towards her parents. 'Best,' she wrote, 'to continue life as normal,' punctuated by school, church activities, and work at Palheiro Gardens, which she would regularly wax lyrical about. So much so that she promised her daughter when they returned to Lisbon, they would certainly plant trees from Madeira in their Restelo garden so that they would always remember life on the island. A story her daughter shared about her mother's determination that they will return to the home of her childhood which was the life she desired for her daughter.

Dom Jose and Senhora Maria de Oliveira Evora arrived in Funchal. The welcoming festive greeting party consisted of their daughter and granddaughter, Sister Francis, a few novices, and members of the extended family. Olga Sara was delirious with excitement to meet her grandparents. After all she knew so much about them from her relatives and seen many photographs. God had answered her prayers, so she now believed they were going to Portugal. Her mother did not betray her expectations as she really did not know the reasons for their visit and her daughter would not find out for many years.

Lia Maria vociferously expressed that the purpose of her parent's visit was to meet their grandchild and arrange their return to Portugal. While in Madeira, it was obvious that they would be interested in meeting people and revisiting places they had not seen for over a decade. Of significant interest was meeting the Goncalves of the Madeira Wine Association. Eagerly accompanying the group led by her parents, she surmised that it was to increase wine export to Europe, as vineyards, especially the most popular French wine regions had been decimated or the cellars ruthlessly pillaged during the war. The wine cellars on Madeira were, on the other hand, well stocked as export virtually ground to a halt during the war and so they could meet the demand.

Wine was cultivated on the island by the early settlers under instructions from 'Henry the Navigator.' As with his other grand plans, he wanted to compete with the Mediterranean producers, if not monopolise the European market, especially as wine makers quickly discovered that the island's climate and soil contributed to the production of some of the best wines in the world. Credit for the industry must be given to the network of Scots who produced blends on the island that were significantly different from European wines.

Supply was always plentiful, as vineyard workers did not drink good wine reserved for the elites, export market, and indeed the Church where, at that period, wine was the preserve of priests at mass and undoubtedly drunk liberally in presbyteries. Workers grew grapes at home and produce some fine 'home grown' *vinho,* commonly referred to by British tasters as 'a good drop.'

Initially, most of the wine and port produced on the island, were exported to Britain after King Charles II banned wines from Europe on marrying Catherine of Braganza. Madeira wine, particularly sherry, was also exported to the British Empire, and became a favourite in the gentleman clubs especially with the British 'overseers' managing sugar cane plantations in the West Indies.

Madeira's success was therefore due to the King. So, his successors did not need to forcefully occupy the island which he did not receive as a dowry, as Britain would come to play a major role in the economic and social development of the islands. Ironically, the famous Madeira cake which accompanies wine was also a British concoction.

Surprisingly, Madeira only produced four types of wine. Serial, a dry white; Verdelho, a golden colour and medium bodied; Malmsey, and *Bual,* medium to dark full-bodied dessert wines. Yet it conquered the global market, and its popularity would lead to many quips, but none better known than Noel Coward's, *'If it's too late for sherry and too early for port, ring for the Madeira, and have some Madeira, m' dear.'*

The island's wine production and export were managed by the Madeira Wine Association. It was established in the mid-eighteenth century by British settlers Francis Newton and John Leacock, who monopolised the industry having learnt the trade from Dom Joao Jose da Camara, from the Braganza family, an early settler who became one of the largest landowners. Evora business island monopoly supplied cork to the company and unsurprisingly, there were 'arranged marriages' with dowries between these families. Land was generally a highly sought after, feature of dowries. In fact, it was common throughout the Empire and after as ownership of land in Portugal was tightly controlled and seldom offered to those from other regions.

With her parents and daughter, Lia Maria visited the winery in Sao Goncalves twice. Sister Francis joined them on the second visit. Olga Sara remembers her visits fondly as, according to her mother, 'a delightful place on the river.' For her, a simple journal entry summed up the visit. 'My grandparents came to Funchal so that Mom can meet Uncle Manuel.' The purpose of her parents' visit was never disclosed by her mother.

Unearthed was the true purpose of the whirlwind visit, which was not intended to arrange Lia Maria's return to

Restelo or indeed Evora, for that matter. To avoid her being ostracised from the community, but more importantly avoid damage to the family reputation, the de Oliveira Evora family considered it in their best interest that she and her daughter remained in Madeira. Logically, it was considered appropriate as she had already been integrated into the community, rather than returning to Portugal with a fatherless child.

Reports from Sister Francis to her sister Yolanda about her granddaughter was that there were no reports of liaisons with young gentlemen. Therefore, the family thought it best that they facilitate the process. Dom Jose and his father Dom Fernando knew Manuel Goncalves' father and grandfather. Manuel was reportedly a young man 'who showed promise and would make a perfect husband and father'. No mention of this matter was discussed with Lia Maria prior to their arrival and indeed while they were in Funchal, and no record existed.

The summer of 1947 ended with Dom Jose and Senhora Maria's farewelling Funchal without instructions. A parting gift to Lia Maria was a gold lined black music box. When opened a ballerina danced to extracts of Tchaikovsky's Nutcracker Suite. Inside were Portuguese Filigree gold jewellery, gifts from her parents and both paternal and maternal grandparents. Filigree jewellery was made from gold of the highest purity and handed down from generation to generation as adornment for Portuguese women, worn on special occasions and festivities.

Preparations for Christmas always started in early December, but in 1947 it was leading up to Holy Communion Sunday, for seven-year old children to receive the sacrament. A ritual where consecrated bread and wine represent the body and blood of Jesus Christ. It coincided with Olga Sara's birthday. But there was also great excitement as the bishop was scheduled to be in attendance. Preparations of the cathedral began on Saturday morning which required a change of routine, according to Lia Maria's journal as she detailed her daughter's special day. Six-year Olga Sara wrote a child's story of sadness, lost in confusion. Her mother's painful story, emotionally charged, overflowing with love and affection for her daughter. Of her parents, it was a chimera of disdain.

Preparing for bed, watched over by her mother, reciting her frequently rehearsed, but on the eve of the service, perfectly recited prayers, her special white lace dress and mantilla proudly laid out, Lia Maria kissed her daughter good night and asked what would be special for her when she woke up. Olga Sara replied, 'When I go to bed I will be six and when I wake up, I will be seven.'

On her seventh birthday while dressed in full communion regalia, her mother praised her for being 'pretty and intelligent.' From her treasure chest, Lia Maria took out an embroidered pouch. Untying the string, she asked her daughter to stretch her arms out, open both hands, and close her eyes. Her mother placed a pair of earrings in her daughter's hands as she opened her eyes to a surprise that lasted generations. Proceeding ritualistically, she gently hooked them on the child's pierced ears explaining that 'these earrings were your great grandmother's and now they are yours.'

The daily ritual of mother and daughter walking to school resumed after the conclusion of religious ceremonies and celebrations for holy communion. Reluctantly returning to school and having to 'put away those special earrings' in the embroidered pouch were her biggest disappointments. A special section of the musical ballerina jewellery box was reserved many years later for those earrings. Other jewellery was kept in less significant boxes and at other locations.

Olga Sara recalled excitedly skipping her way to school on that cool early December morning, holding her mother's hand tightly as she sensed her mother was sad. Which she would write later saying, she wanted to 'make her mother happy.' Kissing her daughter goodbye, Lia Maria reminded her to be at the gate near where the statute of the Virgin Mary was when she first went to school, until it was removed without anyone saying anything about it. And as regular as she had been doing for four years, Olga Sara said, '*Sim Mae*' (Yes Mum.)

That faithful Tuesday Lia Maria was assisting in the design of a new feature of *Jardim Palheiro*. A new range and variety of roses from the garden of Josephine Bonaparte, wife of Napoleon, was to be planted in a special location. For the Empress. Lia Maria would learn, 'roses were an obsession.' Making her the first person to start the collection. Napoleon instructed his troops in the empire to bring rose plants to France, confirmed by the two hundred and fifty variety of roses at her estate, *Malmaison,* which formed the genesis of early French rose cultivation. Illustrated by botanical artist Pierre Joseph Redoute, in his book, *Les Roses*, he presented every variety of rose during the period of her reign. From this book and in her honour, Palheiro planned the rose garden for wealthy European holiday makers arriving on cruise ships for a break from the destruction in those countries.

Apparently, Lia Maria was excited to be on the team designing a new feature of the garden as it was being developed in recognition of Camille Saint-Saëns and in preparation for a marble statue of the composer. The visiting pedantic French garden designer Pierre Letellier was not to be kept waiting. From all accounts, Lia Maria was also looking forward to the meeting, to avail herself of the opportunity to speak French. She did not have an opportunity to practise her French, as Portuguese and English, are the languages commonly spoken in Madeira. Yolanda, her grandmother, taught her French and imbued in her the love of the language with its nuanced formalities so she was pernickety with pronunciations. And reminded herself to ensure she addressed people she did do not know with the formal *'vous'* and not informal *'toi.'*

Standing alone waiting for her mother after school seemed an eternity to Olga Sara as she lost count of the number of times, she recited the multiplication table in English and Portuguese. Growing increasingly agitated, the child wept gently but uncontrolled, it turned into a torrent of tears. She could not understand as she was waiting at the place her mother told her to and knew that she had never waited so long for her mother to meet her after school. From the school, novices were anxiously pulling aside lace curtains and peering through glass paned windows, as all the children had been taken home by their parents, and the orphans were taken by the nuns to prepare for vespers and tea.

Sister Francis recorded in the school's report of being mortified to hear of the child being alone at the gate. Simultaneously, as if running in synchronisation Olga Sara's tears were filled with emotion of desperation. In frenetic and frenzied activity, the confused child was amid general confusion at the convent. Olga Sara was familiar with the orphanage. She was schooled with the orphans and visited them many times with her mother and saw the novices helping the very young children, so she knew she 'did not want to stay there' to wait for her mother. Petulant in anguish, she is reported to have said, 'I am not an orphan,' a statement that resonated with Olga Sara's daughter Carmelita who would come to call herself and brothers orphans when her mother died but without knowing the significance of what she had said.

Lia Maria was allegedly missing, and Olga Sara did not have to stay in the orphanage. Sister Francis was given special dispensation by Mother Superior for the child to remain under her personal care. Seeming like eternity to the child, it was only a matter of a week when she had to move to the orphanage, as she refused to stay with her relatives in her home without her mother. Imagined by then she must have resigned herself to her fate. Sister Francis, who no longer taught, had time to visit her regularly at nights, Olga Sara could not settle at the orphanage as she cried most of the night and disturbed the other girls who did not like her staying there anyway, as she was decidedly 'not one of them.' Years later she wrote 'how little did I know.'

The Goncalves family requested that the child stay with them until her mother returned, but this was deemed inappropriate as although Manuel seemed to like her calling him uncle, it was not approved by Olga Sara's grandparents or Sister Francis. The final and seemingly most suitable, and a solution preferred by everyone was for her to stay with Isabella and Cristobel.

Searches of Palheiro and the surroundings hills were conducted under the direction of the police, with assistance from the convent and cathedral staff. Perturbed with the events, Palheiro garden owners and staff regularly searched and regularly appealed to the police. Church authorities were unrelenting in their quest for the missing young lady. Questioned, the French garden designer who spent most of the day with Lia Maria, was allegedly visibly upset blurted out, '*merde, ce qui se passe ici.*'

Arrogant in anger, he believed, his professionalism was not being respected by the authorities in their quest for a solution to the mystery, in which he apparently was the prime suspect. Needing to find a perpetrator the police implied their meeting was a tryst. Regular searches on the estate, surrounding hills and cliffs found no trace of Lia Maria. The development of the 'Josephine Rose Garden' was postponed as Pierre Letellier left Madeira cleared of any wrongdoing. A family member said, ironically, it was a 'truly fitting outcome as he returned and completed the rose garden.'

Lia Maria de Oliveira Evora's seven years and seven months in Madeira ended abruptly. She never returned as she had promised her child. Rather, it was with a Requiem Mass, Memorial of Seven Novenas, and a liturgy for 'a reserved talented young lady with an unrealised artistic flair.' Arranged by Mother Superior and officiated by the bishop at the cathedral, the outpouring of mourning lasted for many days and for a lifetime by her daughter. Hours of the ceremonial service appeared mystically in a cornucopia of Palheiro most exquisite flowers serving several purposes: prayers and blessings for 'disappeared' Lia Maria and farewell to Olga Sara and Isabella, who were bidding '*despedida Solene*' to the island and expressions of gratitude for the kindness of its people.

Reflecting when she was facing challenges as a seventeen-year old, Olga Sara wrote, 'On leaving Funchal time and place died.' For her, living in the past would not help to repeat it. Memories were a privilege. Reflecting from a distance, she thought that laying the past aside was the only way to settle in Sao Paulo, which was her new home with a new life, hoping someday this day will be worth remembering.

BRAZIL COLONY AND EMPIRE

Brazil is a Federation of twenty-seven states and the largest and most populous country in South America. It occupies approximately half of the continent. Colonised by Portugal, its violent conquering and settlement was a brutal clash of European and the indigenous population followed African civilisations which produced a 'mestico' nation.

The country nevertheless became the most important colony of Portugal, and for a period, the seat of the Portuguese Empire. Brazil was settled as part of the Portuguese quest for gold, following the 'Spanish conquistadors' who found gold and silver in other parts of the continent. But empires did not only plunder for gold. Other minerals were mined but only became major industries centuries later. Brazil's colonial wealth was initially agricultural - sugar cane and coffee. Both produced 'gold.'

The rapid colonisation and spread of Portuguese settlers opened the Amazon to widespread agriculture. Sugar cane production was the major source of revenue for Brazil and Portugal and it made the former the centre of the Empire. When Napoleon occupied Portugal, the monarchy and government moved to Salvador, Bahia in the Northeast making Brazil the centre of the Empire and Portugal a colony. During this period, the two countries operated as a single entity. King John VI declared himself Emperor.

Rio de Janeiro replaced Salvador and many of the Portuguese institutions and industries were recreated contributing to Brazil's social, economic, and political system modelled on Europe. Once Napoleon was defeated, the Portuguese government reconstituted in Lisbon and called for the return of King John VI. He initially resisted, but when he agreed to return to Lisbon, he appointed his son Pedro as Regent of the Kingdom in Rio.

This decision heralded the beginning of a turbulent relationship between Brazil and Portugal. Brazil resisted being subjugated to Portugal and wanted to break the economic dependency as the country was not prepared to keep financing the colonies. It was an independent nation that needed to pursue economic development and finance exploration of the country. Brazil's decision became the harbinger for the demise of the Portuguese Empire and the rise of the Federation which contributed to the struggle that developed among citizens on how they would identify themselves.

This morass led to the encouragement of more Europeans to migrate to Brazil setting in motion Brazil's enduring 'crisis of identity.' This formed a significant aspect of Olga Sara de Oliveira Evora's struggle with identity and why she was referred to as 'the Portuguese lady.' Yet she had never lived on the Iberian Peninsula. Admittedly, Madeira is a municipality of Lisbon. Compounding her cognitive dissonance, she was also struggling with her inherited identity which although an open secret with her family, was never openly spoken about. She never understood the reasoning.

European migration reached its pinnacle when a group of miners from Sao Paulo found gold in Minas Gerais (General Mines) which led to the opening of the interior to prospecting. Finally, as the Portuguese had anticipated, there was gold in Brazil, but now it also had other minerals which led to mining booms, leading to an influx of other European settlers to the interior of the country.

PRESERVE THE CULTURE

Seven-year old Olga Sara Maria de Oliveira Evora's introduction, impression and expectations of Brazil were established with her arrival in Sao Paulo on 18 December 1947.
All she knew and ever cared for was the island settled by
the Portuguese five centuries earlier. She never thought she
would leave Funchal until her mother failed to return to St
Francis Convent School to take her home.

A modern and the largest city in Brazil, Sao Paulo
retained little of its origins and did not have much in
common with Funchal except that it was settled by the
Portuguese. The state always attempted to assert its unique
development and culture to differentiate itself from other
parts of the country through retaining its Portuguese heritage and building a European-wide culture. Its defeat in a
three-month civil war in the 1930s was the turning point of
its role in Brazil, along with post-war industrialisation and
an influx of European migrants.

Sao Paulo became the industrial and coffee centre of
the country and the leader of its export industry. Rivalry
with Rio de Janeiro, which was the capital city until 1960,
became legendary as Sao Paulo had always asserted and
promoted itself through its wealth and power, for domina-
tion of the country.

Settled by ship-wrecked sailors who cohabited with the indigenous Indian community, these men took 'wives' with impunity. It was members of the Society of Jesus who named the place after Saint Paul as it was the saint's feast day. Father Manuel da Nobrega has been acknowledged as the driving force in the development of the state and accumulation of wealth. The religious orders played a significant role in the colonisation and exploration and economic development of Brazil. They built a vast network of religious communities throughout the country and indeed in Latin America. In the process, the Church owned vast land holdings, sugar plantations, and cattle ranches.

The Society of Jesus was founded by a Spanish soldier, Ignacio de Loyola, in the 1530s to convert Turks to Christianity. It was a turbulent period for the Catholic Church. The Inquisition was still actively pursuing transgression and Martin Luther was advocating and demanding changes which led to the Reformation and divisions in the Church. Before that period, Catholicism was the only Christian religion in the world.

Agreeing with Luther, as did many others in the ecclesiastical community, that the Church had to change if it were to survive, Ignatius of Loyola, however, did not want to divide the Church. Rather, he was seeking reformation from within. In the turmoil they skilfully manipulated the Pope who approved the establishment of the Society of Jesus, evident from the volume of letters Ignatius wrote to Popes. Clearly founded on diplomacy, avoiding any similarities with the Templars, as Ignatius knew that the Pope would not have endorsed another military order. Instead, the Jesuits appeal was through universal education.

The culture and practices of the Knights Templar inherited by the Order of Christ had not been acknowledged by the Church as having similarities with the practice of the Society of Jesus. The Templars were a Catholic military order established in 1119, twenty years later they were sanctioned by the Pope. The order was eventually abolished in 1312. Although Templars were persecuted and burnt at the stake and their massive wealth seized in other European countries where they practised, in Portugal the Templars were not persecuted. They became the Order of Christ.

Jesuits actively recruited members from wealthy families and sought them as patrons. 'They had the right to lie in the service of God,' according to their detractors. A fiercely hierarchical organisation, it developed one of the most powerful networks designed to spread their philosophy and influence. So successful were the Jesuits, that they influenced Popes and were advisers to the monarchy in Portugal and, to a lesser extent, in Spain.

Early in its development, the Society wrote its own constitution which has since influenced many individuals and institutions. The most famous example was Cecil Rhodes who developed a mining empire in Southern Africa. Rhodes lives in perpetuity having gifted an eponymous scholarship in 1902 for students to attend Oxford

University. Using the Jesuit constitution as a model, it was executed by the czar of the Rothschild banking dynasty who was also a member of the House of Lords.

In Brazil, the Jesuits saw the Amerindians, (native Indians), as ideal subjects for conversion. The local administration with assent from the Portuguese government set about protecting them almost immediately on a settlement. The Jesuits wanted to protect the Amerindian from Portuguese settlers who were constantly looking for labourers to work on the plantations. According to the Jesuits, they did not have the stamina to endure hard physical labour.

To avoid them being captured by marauding 'bandeiras' that went into the hinterlands to find gold and silver and capture Amerindians to work as slaves, the Jesuits did not teach them Portuguese and even armed them against the bandeiras. Ironically, Sao Paulo honoured the bandeiras with monuments and place names. For example, the state governor's residence was named *Bandeirantes Palacio.*

Proclaimed and widely acknowledged as the *'Guardooes'* (keepers) of Sao Paulo, the Jesuits became responsible for all aspects of the development of the state, from education to migration, including the city's ethnic and social composition. Far away from Salvador and Rio de Janeiro, which were successive capitals of Brazil, the Jesuits unhampered, positioned themselves to determine, design and develop the future of Sao Paulo.

Concerned early in its development, they appealed to the Portuguese King to send orphans and prostitutes to

marry mesticos to 'whiten' the population. Another practice instituted was ensuring that the mother's name was
given to the children to demonstrate their Portuguese
lineage, qualifying them to be a member of the elite. This
practice contributed to families being able to trace their
ancestry to the state's early settlers.

The control and dominance of Sao Paulo by Jesuits
went unchallenged for over a century until landowners
wanted to enslave Amerindians. Using its immense power
and wealth, Jesuits appealed to the crown, sparing the
Amerindians the indignity of being enslaved on their own
land. The Pope issued an order of ex-communication for
enslaving indigenous people. In 1537 Pope Paul III issued a
Papal Bull (*Sumbilis Deus*) in which he declared that: 'The
Indians were endowed with reason, and their lives and
property were, therefore, to be respected.'

Jesuits controlled and directed thousands of Amerindians who were privileged, as opposed to millions of
African slaves who laboured in the sugar cane industry.
This was a great contradiction for the Jesuits. On the one
hand, they successfully fought the Portuguese and Brazilian
governments to protect the Amerindians and on the other,
accepted the practise of enslaving Africans.

In cahoots with the military and landowners, the
administration accused the Jesuits of enriching themselves and their Order as they had established successful
commercial agricultural enterprises using Amerindians.
Complaints from settlers led to the Jesuits being expelled

and their property confiscated. It resonated strongly with them as replicating the Templars' experience.

The Amerindians lost their protector. The Franciscans and Benedictine Catholic Orders tried to take the place of the Jesuits but did not have the same organisational network that the Jesuits built throughout the empire. From an early stage in the development of the country, with the approval of the Pope, Jesuits established a network of churches under an Apostolic Administration.

Allowed to return, the Jesuits influence had waned as by then landowners and the military had assumed a much more significant role in the country. Land reform was not addressed, and elites, supported by the police and military, continued to control the economic development of the country.

With its influence on religion, education and commerce, the Catholic Church became a powerful force in Brazil, as it did on the rest of the continent. Along with the Jesuits, the Franciscans, and to a lesser extent the Carmelites, also contributed to the expansion of the education system and were influential in the development of institutions for higher education. The Jesuits, however, failed in their plans to develop universities as the policy of the Portuguese government was all higher education was to be in the 'motherland.' Not until independence in 1822, did it change.

Ownership of land had been in dispute since settlement and continued to reverberate four centuries later. Struggles over claims that ownership had been manipulated were justified because it could not be verified as early records were destroyed. In the post-war period, violence was a regular feature as protests increased over land ownership in Sao Paulo. Seeking a better life, people moved closer to the city centre, as their land on the outskirts was confiscated for infrastructure or special preference residence of gated or walled communities. Poor people were forced to illegally occupy land next to the city where they could more easily find work. It resulted in *favelas* (shanty towns) becoming a feature of Brazil as the police and military enforced 'government land grab.'

Sao Paulo grew more rapidly than any other part of the country by the turn of the twentieth century, a result of industrialisation and the coffee monopoly. Rapid growth also resulted in continuous land disputes. Whether at the behest of democratic governments or military regimes, the police, and armed forces violently suppressed protests. Property titles were initially granted by the state government to its coterie securing long-term commitment to the armed forces. Land reform has not been addressed. It remains a contentious issue.

Jardim das Camelias Marias was a disputed area of Sao Paulo where violence regularly occurred, and ownership of land was contested since the turn of the twentieth century. Frustrated, the federal government finally claimed the area in its entirety, evicted 'squatters' and euphemistically, 'determine ownership.' The land was sold or granted on a preferential basis to those favoured by the administration.

Built on this land in the late 1890s was *Casa das Flores*. A belle epoque of its era standing on a hillside surrounded by expansive land which gave it the privacy the de Oliveira Evora family desired. Surrounded by English box hedge, by the 1950s it was surrounded by a high stone wall which enclosed manicured lawns and gardens with a forested area. By Sao Paulo standards, the mansion was not exceptional but stood out as it continued to expand to accommodate the extended family much to the chagrin of its distanced neighbours. Attached to the mansion was a guest residence and much further on the grounds were small cottages occupied by outdoor workers, such as Mendes, the gardener and general handyman.

Great Aunt Emilia escorted a seven-year-old child, impenetrable in solitude, from Funchal, where for many weeks, tears reigned like torrential rain. There was no palliative cure for her despair and loneliness, except for her tendency to sleep-walk, which she did into Christmas. Waking from an apocalyptic sleep, Olga Sara distinctly remembered stumbling bleary-eyed into an illuminated house elaborately decorated readied for festivities. Impatiently entreating Emilia, her cousins Adelia and Estrelle, had patiently complied on waiting for a week. On waking they irreverently dubbed her the 'barefoot Portuguese sleeping beauty.'

Christmas Eve and Midnight Mass were at that historically appointed time sacrosanct to believers in the Madonna and Child. Their planned magical mystery tour, therefore, had to be postponed giving priority to the Nativity. Resuming after the other ritual of gift-giving, another tradition associated with the birth of Jesus; from which the girls had expectations, except Olga Sara. Yet, she should have. What the Portuguese girl did not wake up to, and would not for many years, was the guarantee that her financial future had been engineered by her great grandmother who she only knew from letters and daguerreotype.

Leaving and returning for the first time to a house ablaze in lights, the child was excited and eager, wanting to see it all immediately. Imagining she could by twirling 360 degrees. Instead, she fell in the hallway, lying on her back at the bottom of the stairs and seeing stars. Recounting this incident for the first time on her fiftieth birthday, Carlos told her, it was an experience she should share with pride as in his play, *Lady Windermere's Fan*, Oscar Wilde quipped, 'We are all in the gutter, some of us are looking at the stars,' to her and everyone's amusement.

Staring up at the highly polished double staircase leading to different wings of the mansion, she recalled her cousins mockingly laughing. Invoking their prerogative, they were scorned by Dona Maria who accompanied them to mass. Instantly, with maternal instinct, she protected the child she had been watching over, 'who slept like an angel,' for the week. Commissioned to comfort and care for her because of the recurring pattern of nightmares that made her sleep-walk and wake in fright.

As a teenager, Olga Sara came to describe her as a 'guarding angel' believing as her mother would regularly tell her that she was being watched over by a guarding angel. Filled with enduring memories of Dona Maria which she recounted, none more regularly than being introduced to the Spanish Poet, Federico Garcia Lorca. Reciting many times, *Antes del Amonecer*, 'Before the Dawn,' *Buit como el amor los arqueros son ciegos*, which must have resonated with the child.

Enigmatic, Dona Maria gave up the habit of a nun, retreating to Buenos Aires to serve as a governess. She eventually returned to join a group which abhorred the treatment of 'street children' that were despised but they overwhelmed Sao Paulo. It was among the many organisations Olga Sara supported in her philanthropic work while maintaining a relationship with Dona Maria until her passing.

When the exchange of gifts was over, sleep did not beckon, so in the frenzied atmosphere, Olga Sara and her cousins skylarked at the heart of the house. All corridors and hallways led to the chaotic, cluttered, high ceilinged, mosaic-floored, cavernous kitchen always prepared for any event: to cook at any hour, any flavour and cuisine from the Empire and its colonies. To those conjured up without notice, as was a regular occurrence, were added to the scars of many it witnessed that were never recorded.

Widely known and recorded, however, was that the heavy booted feet of Dom Pedro were never allowed entry. Surprisingly observant, he chose not to object, pretending he believed in the cooks' superstition. Rather, he bellowed orders down hallways of framed paintings of Brazil and Argentina's flora and fauna, and the latter's snow-capped mountains. All shivered to readjustment creating a cacophony that reverberated and echoed off the kitchen walls.

The Portuguese tiled floor in the reserved space adjoining the kitchen was not trampled on or walked over, but frequently trod on lightly with the sounds of samba, with dancing cooks in tune and on time. Here was the stage of the mansion's beating heart on which dramas of Shakespearean proportions were performed. And all were easily facilitated by the maids who were always prepared, in their confinement by the practically unnoticed door of this voluminous kitchen from where they were expected to stealthy emerge in bondage.

From their vantage point, maids regularly observed a display of newly designed ladies leather shoes with Portuguese cork soles. Imagine them thinking just another parade of fashionable shoes beyond their reach that added to the unneeded collection imprisoned in the box room. An enterprising man, it was Dom Pedro's foray into another field not to be missed in the building of his envisioned dynastic empire. For all comers, however, this kitchen with its fusion of hanging symbols was the heart and soul of the mansion. In keeping with tradition, indentured maids bowed obediently to chores, serving life sentences silently in service to those who are 'to the manor born.'

Granted freedom by the Lady of Casa das Flores, who appeared only to offer praise to the maids, because at call they conjured up a symphony of flavours. So mesmerising, it was worshipped as a high altar with its delicacies of sumptuous cuisine by all who tasted the exquisite dishes of unquestioned flavours and grew accustomed to its permanently infused aroma of santos coffee. A testimony to the parade of passing beans, outflanking spices from the East. Nutmeg sticks stood upright like Iberian soldiers guarding Molokan spices, waiting in silence to join beans in the conquest of new flavours.

All made possible by a family who brought spice to Brazil to serve the empire. But it was not the house that spice built, as Dom Pedro boasted as he indulged in chilli eating contests. A major part of the mansion must have been funded by the people trade. Engulfed, the mansion was in harmony with the flowing garden naturally merging with indigenous and introduced plants, flowers, and vines. Begonias of many varieties, and what was to become Olga Sara's favourite orchid, *cattleya labiate*, Brazil's national flower. All emitting fragrances that permeated Casa das Flores. Fashioned by the artistry of women, allowing the only man, Dom Pedro to reign supreme, except at the altar of sumptuous creativity.

A Christmas they all too well remembered as it led to a new pattern of life. For Olga Sara, the end of festivities led to another day and another year. Interest in school renewed, she waited to learn the routine from nine-year old Estrelle, closer in age, she hoped to emulate her as a way of gaining acceptance. What she observed was an established daily ritual, A tumble and rumble with competing voices rolling into the kitchen after another school day. Pretending to participate, as she could not know as an only child, she was tasting the flavours of their exuberance as they competed for attention. A shy reluctant participant, Olga Sara grew to learn that she was a surprise item on display. Once the initial novelty wore off, however, her cousins grunted at her in an incomprehensible localised Brazilian version of Portuguese as they walked away. Perhaps she would be welcomed on another day. She imagined.

Although Olga Sara was curious, her mother taught her to always listen and observe. Her silent observation was punctuated as she was peppered with questions. She recalled being mesmerised with the tonalities of voices as they jostled linguistically for position, speaking interchange-ably in Portuguese, Brazilian Portuguese with a sprinkling of Spanish, English, and what she learnt later was Arabic. She recalled thinking of the similarities of being at home in Funchal, as it was common to practise for elite families to speak several languages. Regular practice for the girls with a native speaker of Spanish became mandatory, as Emilia wanted them to speak the language unaccented.

Confiding in her journal, Olga Sara noted that life in Casa das Flores was confusing. From simplicity, she landed in the complexity of new people and new mannerisms. With no one to share her inner thoughts, as she had done with her mother, the teenager resorted to journaling and became an avid and meticulous record keeper for the rest of her life. Surprisingly, her expectations set by Emilia, were shattered as it was all too different, and it all happened too quickly. Escaping in silhouettes of the constancy of her mother and imaging a father who never appeared. Reminiscing, she resorted to a well-worn bundle of sepia photographs of her mother's four generations of men dressed in traditional medieval dress and women dressed in black. The eighteenth-century men were attired in modern suits and women wore flowing multicoloured dresses festooned with filigree jewellery.

This was where Olga Sara withdrew to an imagined life, as she wrote, '*no meu corracao*' 'in my heart' they did not want her. She knew Casa das Flores was not her home. Her cousins laughing and running around her in circles calling her '*menina Portuguesa*' 'he Portuguese girl, the torture she endured when she could not find her way around the house and garden. And as no one intervened, it was confirmation of her belief. Her escape was the mere act of writing as it would free her spirit and her soul.

When teased by her cousins, Ophelia, the cook often glanced in Olga Sara's direction, but never at her, as maids learnt to refrain from making eye contact with their superiors. Cringing and wincing, the cook remained bowed to her chores. All the other maids took her lead. Mendes, likewise, never looked or spoke directly to her, always pretending to be busy with chores inside the home and tending the garden. Her cousins ignored all the servants, or pretended to, but betrayed their tendency with a maid's fixed gaze, with pouting lips being bitten. Mendes had a pleasant manner and was always kind and gentle to the household. An object of curiosity, he did not escape the girls' facial displays purposely intended for him. Emulating their father, they looked past Mendes to make sure they looked but did not see him.

Eagerly attending convent school with her cousins, Olga Sara grasped for them to accept her. But she had become used to being ignored and disparagingly being referred to as 'the Portuguese girl,' to tears she could no longer shed. St Francis School was unlike Funchal which was much smaller and friendlier. Along with her mother's presence, there was Sister Francis and the other nuns who were caring and gently guided her at every turn.

Daily mass at her new school, gave Olga Sara a sense of belonging and purpose as was the comfort of Emilia's gaze. School life improved further with the presence of Rossana Camargo as they became 'the best of friends.' Like Olga Sara, Rose was not a 'Paulista.' She came to Sao Paulo from Lisbon when she was six-years old, as her parents decided to leave to escape the war. There was a steady flow of Europeans to Latin American which increased when the war in the Atlantic ceased.

Bea was regularly at Casa das Flores, as she managed Dom Pedro's business, but did not say much to Olga Sara for many years. At dinner, she would attempt to, but it was not surprising as Olga Sara's cousins were boisterous in their domain and had stories to tell that must be listened to as the girls, encouraged by their father, demanded silence. Competing for attention to recount stories about school and friends, especially Paulistas, who their father encouraged them to actively associate with at school outings and holidays. Friends were generally from settler families like the de Oliveira Evora. Notably were the Lacerdas, Vargas and Setubals. As Olga Sara grew older, school outings were more irregular and visits were only to the Camargos, which she reciprocated with Emilia's encouragement. Rose's frequent visits to Casa das Flores was bonding for a lifetime.

Thinking convent school extra-curriculum activities would improve their longing to be at one with the Paulista girls, these two teenagers eagerly looked forward to school excursions. Olga Sara remembered her first excursion very well indeed as she wrote about it fondly because she had to read it to the class. It was about *Praca da Se*, the city's central square scattered with sculptures and fountains, coterminous to the cathedral of the same name, which is the seat of the bishop. It was built on the crypt of the original church settlers and the resting place of the bishops of Sao Paulo. Mass in this cavernous place of worship was a regular part of the convent school liturgical education program where they commemorated feast days in an interior of walls and ceilings and windows of glass displaying reproductions of local products of the state. Pride of place for the nuns was to take the girls to *Patio do Colegio*, the first school built by the Jesuits stamping their imprimatur on education and demonstrating their centrality to the state.

Of all the places she visited, Olga Sara came to prefer *Jardim da Luz* because of its beautiful portrayal of the simplicity of nature. In the ambience of this garden, the teenager came alive as she was finally seeing similarities and took to publicly making comparisons with Funchal. Apart from Rose, she elicited and perhaps solicited others to worship at her altar of nature. Over the years, the garden would increasingly become the backdrop of a city multiplying with skyscrapers, as a result, she no longer worshipped at the temple. As with Buenos Aires, its Argentine competitor, Sao Paulo, also constructed an obelisk on the site of the foundation of the city. Pretentiously borrowing from Egyptian, Roman, and Greek civilisations as if to emulate greatness. Simultaneously, dismantling and eradicating the great civilisations of the land they occupied. Even the cities' architecture, a mixture of baroque and neoclassical modelled on European buildings was intended to remind the settlers of home. What these colossal structures signified contributed to a rivalry and a tale of two cities.

It was almost five years before Olga Sara's place at school was recognised. Music contributed to the growth of her popularity. Her new music teacher, Sister Josephine, realised that her piano playing was now far advanced in comparison to her contemporaries. And not only from examinations but her knowledge of music and her stylistic meandering at the keyboard.

The playing of Eric Sate No 1 Symphony, was the composition that brought her to the school, parents, and other Paulista's attention when she played at an assembly for the visiting bishop of Rio de Janeiro. Received warmly, except by her cousins, her popularity with the other girls grew, especially with Rose. The Portuguese girls had been accepted and they were now all her friends. The report in the Parish Magazine, *Luz Azul,* assured her of popularity. But she was still being identified by her origins: Portuguese not Brazilian and certainly not Paulista.

Credit for her music must always be sheathed home to her mother, Lia Maria. In her generosity, however, Olga wrote and publicly praised her and great aunt Emilia for significantly contributing to her improvement. Emilia was not only a fine pianist but a teacher with patience and empathy. Always at the ready to take Olga Sara under her care, which she knew 'the child' needed, but waited 'until she knew the child was ready.' Many years later it was part of a conversation they had when they were being fare-welled. Perceived attention to her at times caused friction with her cousins. But Emilia was reassuringly there for all of them.

Olga Sara's life at Casa das Flores revolved around Emilia, Ophelia, and Mendes. And at school with Rose and Sister Josephine. Older than her, Adelia and Estrelle's time was spent with their friends visiting or when they recipro-cated or on excursions. They never invited Olga Sara, and always gave purportedly plausible reasons for not including her in their lives. 'She is a Portuguese girl, not a Paulista,' boisterously invoked with a certain pride.

Olga Sara would come to write, 'it dashed my hopes and confidence in myself.' weighed down by the magnitude of her imagined solitude, believing she would never become 'one of them.' Sao Paulo was advocated as the beacon of Brazil's future because of its wealth, industrialisation, and culture. Residents, specifically elites from establishment families, take great pride in being called 'Paulista.'

'You know,' journaling about her great aunt, 'she would never ask them to apologise.' It was an emotional seesaw. These words exist in her journal written in a deliberate hand. Emilia told Olga Sara, she refrained from intervening in teenager girls squabbling. These opportunities her great aunt saw as contributing to assisting Olga Sara to learn and for self-improvement. After all, she was an only child and did not have to accommodate others. Resorting to explain by using the scales and chords of a piano. Intuitively, she would come to detect when Emilia wanted to teach her 'life's lessons.' Her most memorable was when Emilia played and sang a theme song which she bequeathed to her. From Cole Porter,

'Experiment, make it your motto day and night,
experiment it will lead you to the light... be
curious, though interfering friends may frown, ...
Get furious at each attempt to hold you down...
This advice, I am sure you will endure.'

Although she liked and hence introduced Olga Sara to the life and music of Cole Porter, who she respected for his formulation of synonyms in the English language and his preppy demeanour, she was reticent about other aspects of his life. A subject they discussed when she knew Olga Sara was ready.

Their favourite past time was indulging in reciting and discussing poetry and the classics of English literature. Emilia's favourite poet was the Cuban didact, Jose Marti, 'I have a white rose to tend.' Olga Sara's favourite, however, was Henry Wadsworth Longfellow's, the Daffodils. When reciting the poem, she would always jump up, arms outstretched like a bird in flight looking at the sky reliving her childhood. 'I wander lonely as a cloud…but danced with daffodils,' as she tried her best to emulate her mother. Olga Sara remembered and treasured memories of the first time she recited the poem and Emilia told her about the beauty of the English countryside and especially the Lake District with mountains and lakes where Longfellow lived and wrote the poem as a homage to its beauty.

None of these activities was ever part of their repertoire when Dom Pedro was at home. At those times Emilia would get Olga Sara to play her choice of music, which was inevitably Eric Sate's piano recitals. Then, as they routinely did on such occasions, they would have coffee and their favourite Portuguese custard tart in the garden. Where they discussed the progress of the new rose garden which was by then looking more permanent from the horticultural pruning with solemn expertise. Thanks, Olga Sara sighed, remembering her mother, but it was Mendes, wishing she could congratulate him about his 'green fingers.' Occasionally, Dom Pedro would come into the garden and comment on Olga Sara's music but not her roses. It became the purview of her and Emilia.

Dom Pedro was self-assured but covetous and capricious. Large in stature at six feet, two inches, with a ruddy complexion, brown eyes, and black, slightly wavy hair. The Dom spoke with an air of command in a stentorian voice, like a high-ranking military officer, despite not serving in the armed forces. In fact, like many wealthy families, they provide a litany of reasons for avoiding the twelve-month compulsory military service in Portugal and Brazil. Vicariously, he learnt to command from his cohort of high-ranking career officers. But it was well-known by the establishment of his association with officers. According to records and press reports, he unquestionably developed military instigated plans and championed projects, such as building roads to access the Amazon basin. Consolidating more than a century of a symbiotic relationship between his family and career officers for mutual benefit.

Brazil's history is littered with civilian and military governments' intermittent plans to develop infrastructure to assist with improving the socio-economic conditions of the country. Always for the benefit of the people. Under this pretext, military, more so than civilian governments, designed projects to monitor and curtail insurgents and guerrilla activities that seeped across its borders, especially from Uruguay.

The part of Brazil where the de Oliveira Evora family had extensive business was in Bahia, in the northeast of the country. Dom Pedro was on its capital, Salvador's business council and cathedral committee. For holidays, he took the entire family, including cook and some maids, but never Mendes, to their belle epoque in Salvador where they spent Christmas. In Salvador, they witnessed the frivolity of the music and dance of carnivals. Salvador's festival is not as well-known as its counterpart in Rio de Janeiro. The city was the site of the first carnival, which was the best, according to Brazilians, as it enveloped the entire city. Carnival ushered in self-sacrifice before fasting for Lent, so a culture of excess was associated with Rio's but not Salvador's. From Olga Sara's perspective, it was the most enjoyable family holiday. For her, carnival on her seventeenth year would become the most memorable and would come to have a significantly unwelcomed and unplanned impact on her life.

BAHIA: ENGINE OF EMPIRE'S GROWTH

The legacy of Portuguese colonisation of Brazil impacted most significantly on the Northeast. It left a legacy and a system of large plantations concentrated in the hands of a small group of Portuguese settler families, entrenched in amassing wealth at the expense of poor peasant farmers and slaves. With support from the Monarchy and Church, these families controlled the sugar cane driven economy, which was the most important export and major revenue source for Portugal and Brazil for over three centuries.

To satisfy Europe's increasing appetite for sugar and generate revenue to develop Brazil and Portugal, it was necessary to find workers to meet the needs of the rapidly growing sugar cane plantations. It was decided to capture indigenous Amerindians to work the fields. Hunting and capturing the native people from the Amazon, in places closest to Bahia, was pursued with gusto.

To achieve their objectives, wealthy landowners with private armies, accompanied by Jesuits, set up 'marauding hunting parties' commonly known as *bandeiras,* so-called because of the flags they carried bearing their insignia. Amerindians were easy prey. The sight of horses ridden by heavily armoured Portuguese men thundering towards them, scattered partly clothed natives in fear to seek protection which Jesuits provided. Easy prey, they were herded into clusters, suffering claustrophobia. Forced to work on plantations led many to die from exhaustion toiling in the direct heat of the sun. In the Amazon, they lived under the canopy of trees.

As plantation owners looked for new workers, the Jesuits saw an opportunity to use the Amerindians in other industries in the Amazon, in places and conditions which they were accustomed to. Brazilwood was highly sought after in Europe for its enduring qualities and sustainability. With no constraints, landowners logged that species of trees to extinction. Successfully arguing against this rapacious practice, the Jesuits were granted the monopoly for sustainability and export. With Amerindians, they made the crop productive so that the logs became the country's other major export after sugar. Amerindians were now seen as more suitable for forestation and agriculture. Industriously, the Jesuits were the most numerous and enterprising of all the religious orders in Brazil.

A compromise for landowners was to import African slaves. They were accepted as better equipped to work on sugar plantations as they were stronger, easier to discipline and more persistent with their work. Acknowledged by the Crown as a perfect solution, they imported slaves from the west coast of Africa, which Portugal had colonised and was directly across the Atlantic from Bahia.

The voyage across the Atlantic was arduous for them.

Often violently captured and enslaved, conditions onboard the ships were not equipped for 'human cargo' resulting in many being injured and died. The ship's crew did not enter the cargo hold for fear of being attacked by these desperate people. Arriving in the capital city, Salvador, they were kept in barracoons before being sold to plantation owners.

Antonio Vieira, a Jesuit, who was an adviser to the Duke of Braganza also influential with the de Oliveira Evora family, tried unsuccessfully to make a similar impact for the Africans as the Jesuits had done for the Amerindians. A remarkable man, Viera also fought for Jews not to be subjected to the Inquisition, as it was claimed that many who had converted to Christianity were secretly practising Judaism. This Jesuit's pleas had limited impact on successive Portuguese and Brazilian administrations.

Abject failure by the Jesuits meant that African slaves soon became the backbone of Brazil's primary agricultural product: sugar cane. For plantation owners to achieve their increasing quotas, according to an Evora Jesuit, 'slaves' bodies were broken by work without end.' In rapid succession, large plantations proliferated on the Northeast coast and Bahia became the place where large sugar cane estates (*Fazendas*) and mills dotted the landscape.

Although sugar cane was the major source of revenue, slave trading was the next most profitable business for Portugal and Brazil, and for many families such as the de Oliveira Evora. As a result, the state of Bahia, especially its capital, became the most Africanised state of Brazil. With the size of the African population concentrated in the state, rebellion and other hostility became endemic. Dubbed, 'slave revolts,' they were brutally suppressed by the private armies which became the core of the Brazilian police and armed forces. Portuguese slave owners unable to impose control resorted to segmenting slaves based on tribal allegiance. For the slaves, however, ethnicity and tribal differences disappeared as they realised they were all in the same position.

The size of the African population also impacted significantly on Portuguese culture. Creolised beliefs and practices developed from a combination of tribal worship practices and Catholicism. The vivacity of the Afro-Catholic religious processions and feast day celebrations were reflected in the churches, convents and statues of the Virgin Mary which proliferated the city.

The cathedral in Salvador was influenced by Jesuits. Entering, Olga Sara recalled being blinded by the light. Seeking an answer, she wrote, it was answering God's call: 'Let there be light.' It was the response she received from a Jesuit. The iconography was elaborate with a stained-glass window, the decorative interior was pronounced and overstated to convey messages and sayings from the Bible for illiterate people. Communication through imagery was the established practice as education was not seen as a necessity in the early period. After the cathedral, the Franciscan church became the most important in the city because of its shimmering gold interior, highlighting that it was built during the gold rush.

Salvador became the spiritual and cultural heart of the Northeast with its kaleidoscopic colours and the diversity of people. From her first visit, it came to influence Olga Sara's creativity and fertile imagination. She wrote 'A garden of many colours and hews is more interesting than one of just one colour.' Originating from a small island in the Atlantic with memories of Palheiro gardens, she was now in a country she could not comprehend, so large and diverse that it was unimaginable.

Narrow cobblestone streets led to baroque mansions and churches with straight lines, pastel facades and square towers reflecting their Portuguese heritage. The de Oliveira Evora mansion was in the *Cidade Alta*, or upper city. This was the family home during their twice-yearly visits to Salvador, but a regular residence of Dom Pedro.

During these visits, the young girls regularly sought permission from Dom Pedro to visit their family's *Fazenda*. Curiosity piqued their interest based on the proliferation of stories that was perpetuating a 'postcard' image of a fallacious fantasy. They longed to visit a mill to find out how sugar and molasses were produced as it captured their inquisitiveness. From Dom Pedro's perspective, telling Emilia, 'it was just that, and best left that way.' But he never gave any explanation for his decision. Years later none of them could explain their obsession with molasses as children. Assuming because it was used in their favourite savoury and sweet dishes. Just as often as they requested, it was just as often denied. Finally they resigned themselves to never having an opportunity to visit a sugar plantation as the maid told them *Fazendas* were not for young ladies. Dom Pedro, as all the family knew, was not to be disobeyed. Perpetuated in the family and spreading beyond, his word was 'gospel.' All must be accepted without explanation.

In her seventeenth year, and after a decade in Brazil, Olga Sara was reportedly a self-confident young lady. With her cousins at college in Florida, she was now for the first time on her own with the family for carnival. Her commitment to the Church was reflected in how she emulated her mother. She assisted the nuns with the orphans and was always eager to conduct a 'sing-a-long' playing the piano. Through her activities, she developed an affinity with Salvador, facilitated by the family's 'good deeds' and Dom Pedro's role in the church and the community.

Olga Sara's intense curiosity about *Fazendas,* sugar plantations, and molasses was in abeyance for satiation with a poignancy of unrealised expectation. Seeking an opportunity, she confidently believed she did not need to seek Dom Pedro's permission. But perhaps, she thought she should, except she was sure he would insist she adhere to his policy. Olga Sara's guardian until she turned twenty-one was Dom Pedro.

After lunch and time for the children's siesta, Father Thomas de Souza was leaving the orphanage on his way to administer communion to an elderly family member of the owner of a sugar plantation purportedly part-owned by her family. Father de Souza, a Jesuit, with nodding acquaintance to the de Oliveira Evora family, was bidding farewell to the nuns, who were themselves busy with the children. Olga Sara wrote as she was no longer needed, she offered to assist the priest. Her recollection was of him calling out to the nuns who waved goodbye. In innocence, exuberantly took as acknowledgement, if not endorsement for fulfilling her known desire. After all, Father de Souza was purportedly the 'most Jesuitical of the Order in Bahia.'

The drive to the sugar plantation a few miles out of Salvador was in an old truck that portended a bumpy ride on dirt roads, mostly used for transporting sugar cane to the mills. The windows of the truck were open and warm air blew in at irregular intervals as it was dependant on the speed at which the truck was travelling and the velocity of the wind.

Olga Sara sat in silent awe as they drove forever through what were endless fields of sugar cane, green and lush, swaying in the wind or standing resplendent relishing the sun. Paths seemingly crisscrossed, scattered in all directions in the fields which marked the routes to the mills. The height and density of cane surprised her. Momentarily, she was fearful realising, 'how easy' it would be to get lost in the fields. In silence, stifled by her imagination she was in consternation.

Breaking the silence, conversation with the Jesuit was halting and irregular. At his behest, later under psychoanalysis, it was deemed a mechanism of asserting control, as he chose to break the silence to tell her a version of events.

Pointedly about the social development of plantations and stories of owners and workers. A diatribe which heightened a sensitive young lady's fear and anxiety. After all, at seventeen, she neither knew nor understood anything about her family's businesses. And she was indeed not expected to. Emilia never spoke about these matters. For her, Dom Pedro and Bea managed the business, while she was solely responsible for Casa das Flores and 'the girls,' her term of endearment for Olga Sara and her cousins.

Approaching the *Fazenda* on this sunny late morning, she was blinded by the light and recalled from a distance seeing a small, then abruptly arriving at a large rambling old house. Writing her testimony months later, she could not write what she had anticipated. 'I am finally at a Fazenda.' Instead, 'here I was surrounded by a disorganised group of small-thatched huts all shimmering in the hot sun with children in various states of dress mingling in total familiarity with all types of animals but mostly dogs.' Stepping out of the truck they were greeted by a cacophony.

Ushered into the house, Olga Sara walked into an interior of open spaces spreading out ending at closed doors and an open kitchen of enormous proportions cluttered in readiness as if to serve a battalion. She could not but compare it with the de Oliveira Evora home in Salvador. The only similarity was that the house was full of women, men and children were always outdoors. Elderly women were sitting comfortably under slowly turning fans strategically located around the room. Ordered to wait for Father de Souza, Olga Sara in disappointment sat in loneliness in a room crammed with furniture and packages being readied to be taken to the presbytery and orphanage in Salvador.

Mestico *servos femeas*, servants were bringing food and drinks as Father Thomas, she assumed, diligently contemplated a confession and gave communion to the grandmother who was ill. Olga Sara assumed, as no one spoke with her, unlike home, servants were not allowed to speak with distinguished visitors especially as they were also in the company of a distinguished Jesuit priest.

Drifting with fascination, as compellingly her imagination took flight. Interrupted to be reminded of refreshments. On the orders of Father de Souza, she was escorted by a matronly servant of some authority to visit the huts and meet the families. She had no direct exposure to the *Favelas* surrounding Sao Paulo, endemic with squalor in poverty. In a city of plenty, comparisons between the fazendas and huts were depressing for the young lady, as the servant boldly opined. From this experience, Olga Sara would come to advocate education. These children were restricted to Sunday School.

Stepping back into the milieu of the orderly regulated life of the *Fazenda* she was greeted by a priest delighting in her immersion in the life of the workers' families. He knew them well from conducting weekly services in a thatched hut, which was their only opportunity to be dressed in their Sunday best. In the company of a few of the elderly ladies, Olga Sara was excited to tell them about her family and their frequent visits to Salvador withholding the fact that she was visiting without their permission. She, did, however, let them know that she came specially to see the sugar cane fields and mills and to learn about the making of molasses.

In the candour of naivety and oblivious to social status, Olga Sara was ruminating in outrage that *jovems* were not allowed in the fields and mills. Spoken in a creole dialect by the matronly servant and translated or interpreted by the 'wizened old lady' who was the reason for the priestly visitation. Assertively, she requested that Olga Sara sit next to her so that she can have a better look at the child as her eyes 'are not what they used to be.' Trembling hands placed on the young lady's head transposed her to a *de ja veux*, a decade earlier in Funchal. Feeling vulnerable as she was not wearing her amulet.

Gently kissing her head, saying in fluent Portuguese, 'Eu vou orar por voco mew filho,' (I will pray for you, my child.) In her journal, Olga Sara compared these two occasions, speculating that there was a sensory spirituality with old ladies, as they were both intuitive. In the spiritualism of a Bahian, well known throughout the country, did she have a premonition which was at the time thought of as the senility of the elderly? Years later she found out that the old lady was a Camargo, a member of an early settler family. She died that night.

Father de Souza readied himself for the hour's drive to Salvador to return the young lady in bedazzled confusion safely to the nuns who were responsible for her to be escorted home. Bearing a pious demeanour, he silently and in contemplation, packed his bag for vestments, kissing the items as he folded them in readiness for his next mission. Leaving hastily, he was reminded that March was the time of year when storm clouds gathered in the afternoon with an unexpected burst of torrential rain.

Conscious of weather warnings, driver and passenger were contemplating what lay ahead. Olga Sara and Father de Souza, gazing upon the lushness of the passing sugar plantation, saw God's work but questioned the audacity of nature. Rehearsing the story for her friends, but not her family, ruminating she contemplated committing a sin of lying sitting next to a priest. Not serious enough to be classified as a mortal sin, absolution and penance could be dispensed and the sin nullified. Juxtaposing her options, however, punishment for disobeying Dom Pedro's orders would warrant opprobrium. Imagining delirium, Olga Sara committed to sin but decided to endure penance as a plausible option.

She imagined, as Father de Souza drove in silence, that he was contemplating the confession he just heard and the penance he dispensed to a frail old bed-ridden lady, but it was to be a distrustful presumption. At this stage of her life, Olga Sara wondered what sins had this old lady committed to seek repentance and what penance was dispensed? But from what was later uncovered, it was more likely that the priest may have been tormented and battling his own demons, searching for reconciliation with God.

Deep in the depths of doctrinal prognostications, the jovem was interrupted to be told that the lush green fields had to be burnt before being harvested. The stalks were then milled to extract the juice which was dried to produce sugar crystals and a small amount of juice was fermented to produce molasses. Illicit alcohol, which Olga Sara would not have known, or told about, was produced by the slaves to ease the melancholy and pain of their miserable existence. It was all counterintuitive to her expectations. Bumping on their way to Salvador, lightning struck, and darkness descended as storm clouds gathered and roared angrily. Breaking his self-imposed silence, the Jesuit told his charge that he too did not know about sugar cane until he arrived in Salvador.

Father Thomas de Souza was a native of Goa. Olga Sara identified it from the map on the school wall in Funchal where it was shown as part of Portugal. With pride, she told him how she learnt about Goa, by explaining the magic carpet ride. Filled with enthusiasm, the priest was glad to hear her boldly declared, 'Of course I know everything about Goa from the game.' Serendipitously, Father Aloysius from Funchal was also from Gao.

During the post-war era, alternative opportunities were becoming available, so young Europeans were not flocking to the seminaries. Of necessity, priests from the colonies were filling vacancies which continue in the twenty-first century. Perplexed by the physical and linguistic differences of these two men from Goa, she looked at Father de

Souza and declared, 'I am Portuguese.'

In the blissfulness of her innocence, he assumed, according to his evidence, she implied he was not. From those thoughts, she would come to write a treatise on a man who had the most profound impact on her life. Responding to what he believed was a misperception, said in irritated animosity, 'I am also Portuguese.'

Explaining that his father was from Lisbon and his mother was from Goa. The Portuguese used the term miscegenation, which meant 'inter-breeding.' The Monarchy and Jesuits encouraged inter-marriage all over the Empire. Unlike other colonial powers, Portuguese families did not migrate, only men did to develop the colonies and make their fortune. A small country with a small population could not allow its citizens to migrate.

Father de Souza told Olga Sara of his love of Goa and his family of five brothers and four sisters. 1957 was a turbulent year for Goa as it witnessed protests with the Portuguese government in its fight for independence. Although his parents were in Goa, his brothers and sisters had moved to Macao, a Portuguese enclave in China, and other parts of India. He declared he was not close to them as he left home when he was twelve to join the monastery, where one of his older brothers was also studying. But his brother did not take his vows, much to the consternation of his parents. Father de Souza was sent to Salvador after he took his Holy Orders. He was influenced by his father who had enormous respect for the Order of the Society of

Jesus, as they had made a significant impact on the people, especially through education.

GOA HOME

A Portuguese enclave on the western coast of India, incor-
porating Damian and Diu, Goa was colonised early in the
sixteenth century during Portugal's quest to dominate the
spice trade. To achieve their objective, the Portuguese were
determined to defeat the Mohammedans who occupied
the area harbouring historical animosity, they identified
Muslims as Moors, who they defeated during the recon-
questa of Portugal and Spain.

To gain a foothold in Goa, the Portuguese aligned
themselves with the Hindus to rid the area of the Muslims,
destroying all the mosques and unsurprisingly, Hindu
temples. The Portuguese wanted 'to obliterate the Indian
character of the people.' When they converted to Christianity, Indians took Portuguese names and intermarriage
between Indian women and Portuguese men were advocated
to increase the population and embed Portuguese culture.

Fascinated by Goa, seeing it as the meeting place of East
and West, it quickly became the capital of the Portuguese
Empire in the East and considered part of metropolitan
Lisbon. It was, therefore, said that: 'if you see Goa you do
not need to see Lisbon,' as its architecture replicated that
city. There was a proliferation of churches and arches built
in the gothic style which the Portuguese also developed

in Madeira. But in Madeira, they had no resistance as the island was uninhabited, unlike Goa which was a busy fishing port teeming with Indian and Arabian traders.

Global conditions changed rapidly from the sixteenth century as other Europeans were not prepared to continue their dependence on Portugal for spices. Cunningly responding, the English and Portuguese developed 'The Goa Accord,' to jointly exploit the spice trade creating a monopoly. One of the reasons was the desire to thwart the Dutch who were also capitalising on the lucrative spice trade. As a result, Goa's contribution to Portugal's economy became disproportionate to its size.

Carefully observed and admired by the British East India Company for the way it enriched the Portuguese, an interchange of policies and practices was instituted. A record unparalleled for its monopolistic rapacious colony polices, the Company enriched Britain at the expense of India. In collusion with the British government, it was allowed to operate as the colonial administration with an army, not a company, until it outlived its purpose.

In the frenzied atmosphere of asserting power, the Portuguese accelerated Goa's transformation by appointing, Alfonso de Albuquerque, Viceroy, with a mandate to oversee social, political, and economic development. With unfettered authority, the Viceroy replicated Portuguese architecture, as Goa was to become the capital of the Empire in the East. Therefore, it had to develop a municipal council modelled on Lisbon to impose greater Portuguese influence rather than Indian or Hindu. Suppressing resistance at all cost to achieve its objective, it imposed a policy of converting all inhabitants to Catholicism.

To institute its policy, Portugal knew that it required the best and the highest order in the Church. The Portuguese King asked the Pope for Jesuits to be sent to Goa to assist with educating the people and converting them to Christianity. Francis Xavier, a founding member of the Society of Jesus, made it his life's mission to Christianise and educate the people. Educating boys was the very first program instituted. St Pauls Boys School was the first the Jesuits built in Goa and where Father de Souza and his brothers were educated. Girls were low on the list of priority. It was centuries before they were formally educated.

Quickly gaining influence in Goa, the Jesuits convinced the Monarch to give them commercial concessions. Permission granted, the Jesuits amassed great wealth as they courted wealthy merchants and developed agricultural products for export. Jesuits mingled commerce with teaching the Bible as had been their practice since the establishment of the Order and in every colony.

The success of their commercial endeavours in Gao and other places in the East such as Macao led to a culture of excess and resulted in significant criticism. Supposedly, their lavish lifestyle of wearing silk robes, holding regular banquets and establishing a retinue of celebrating all feast days led to the Jesuits in Gao being described as 'sinners,' when in fact they were supposed to be the companions of

Jesus. Jesuits who were accused of seeking worldly rewards, contrary to their vows, were subjected to the Inquisition in Rome, dispelling the misnomer of 'The Spanish Inquisition' which was in fact 'The Vatican Inquisition.'

Olga Sara was enthralled and excited about the lesson, as she had learnt so much more about another part of the Portuguese empire. Or she may have been too young to comprehend the complexities when she learnt about Goa at school in Funchal. She said her mother would have been disappointed that she had not remembered more about it from those lessons. Whatever was happening, in her words, Olga Sara vowed that she 'became mesmerised,' in this encounter. Her heightened senses led her to transfix her gaze on the priest, she admitted. It resulted in her unknowingly experiencing transference, common in such situations, according to a psychoanalyst in New York, who would assist her to manage her trauma.

Mesmerised in transference, the torrential downpour brought the reality of rain, compelling her to immediately switch her gaze from the priest to wind up the truck's window as the water was enveloping the truck. Father de Souza's frequent visits to the region made him knowledgeable about the contours of colonial plantations, where the gutters ran in the middle of the road preventing vehicles from being stuck in the mud. This is a design still evident in heritage-listed villages in Latin America. Navigating the route to shelter, he veered off the muddy track, delivering them into an abandoned sugar mill.

By the 1960s, mills in a state of disrepair proliferated the countryside. Foreign companies exploited the situation which was described by social scientists: *dependencia.* Multinational companies created markets in the developed countries luring businesses in developing countries to become dependent on them. Creating dependency and then capitalising on it, they acquired and consolidated sugar plantations owned by settler families. Multinational companies took advantage of this situation, corporatising the businesses to maximise their value in concert with financial institutions. By listing the corporations on global stock exchanges, in one fell swoop maximising their return on investment by multiples. Financial institutions became the harbingers of complex company structures that benefit the few, disadvantaging many.

Rain from the torrential downpour, propelled by the force of the wind, resulted in water cascading on the walls of the mill. Added to the bellowing of thunder and intermittent flashes of lighting heightened Olga Sara's anxiety. Uncertainty challenged her security. Trembling from a cold fever, she could not understand as she saw steam rising. Dashing into the old mill overgrown with a profusion of vines and plants bending from the weight of the water, she was transported in images of Madeira. As thunder roared and dark clouds stole the light, she knew that there is always a crack to let the light in and in that shaft of light, she searched for the 'spirit of her mother, seeking comfort,' who she believed appeared in silhouette. Foretelling it would rain for forty days and nights, trapping them in repentance in Salvador.

Which, Olga Sara, would come to elaborate in a treatise many months after the incident, instead of, as a regular journal entry. Afraid and alone with despair she screamed as Father de Souza held her to offer his warm body for comfort. In his clutch, however, she could not find safety. Yet she remembered a priest preaching, 'you must believe in God as in your darkest hour, he is the Light.' Wet and trembling from fear, she did not want to be comforted by anyone but her mother. Remembering in Funchal she always resorted to escaping in her embrace for safety. But in Salvador, she was not sure what it would be with Emilia and Dom Pedro. Envisaging, as they regularly did, they would have visitors. Praying to be in communion with God, begging for forgiveness as she had disobeyed Dom Pedro. Knowing he was always right. The uncertainty induced stress.

Escaping to seek solace by evoking the soul of her spirituality, she was pious. Olga Sara recalled her senses being heightened, alerted to the sound of thunder growing louder as it rained heavier, forcing them further into the mill steaming from water evaporating in the heat. Forecasting from experience, Father de Souza reassured her that it will soon be over as he held her, and she rebuked his unsuspecting amorous intentions. Remorseful for resisting, she should have known not to as Catholic children were indoctrinated to trust priests and nuns.

Spontaneously, she recalled the vision of being scolded by her mother for resisting Father Aloysius's plea for a hug. Captive to the dilemma of her quandary, without realising or consenting, Father de Souza squeezed her as he pushed her onto the dusty floor strewn with burnt and dried sugar cane leaves heaped in a corner as water trickled its way forming puddles at their feet. In consternation, horrified, she lost her innocence, not understanding the reasoning.

Screaming and appealing to her mother and her God during a tropical rainstorm was never going to attract the attention she desperately needed, from either of them. 'Momentarily,' she would come to write, in the midst, of lush cane fields, pulsating with sheaths of rain, ecumenism was not in her grasp. But she had not been abandoned. Rather, it was apocalyptic. Although she was mired in fear, she never gave in and prayed that the roof would collapse by the will of God, so that it would be all over in an instant. And in that very instant. Olga Sara recounted that she prayed for divine intervention from a terrestrial finger-pointing from that saintly hand. Easy to envisage as she was elevated by an 'out of body experience,' from high above in the dark clouds. Divine light, however, appeared through fractures in the thatch. Praying to the Virgin Mary, as she believed in the Immaculate Conception, she lost her virginity and her faith.

Holding her, as she was shaking uncontrollably in fits of tears, Father de Souza clumsily tried to console the young lady, telling her it was their special bond, confusing her into a paralysis of her spirit. Aiming for tranquillity, kneeling, he offered a silent prayer and delivered absolution as he made the sign of the cross and said the *Pater Noster*. Invoking the Holy Spirits, his prayers were answered, the dark clouds cleared, but never from her soul. Despite attempts, she could never recall the journey to Salvador. Therapeutically and physically, she remained in a disassociated fugue.

Lamenting on her misfortune to her journal, she confused her arrival with her departure and as a result, she caused much confusion at the convent where the chauffeur anxiously waited, as storm clouds gathered. Rehearsing her predetermined plans, all that mattered was her performance. Documenting the incident years later, as she had broken her rule by not entering the incident in her journal at the time, demonstrated what at seventeen she expected of herself. Unpretentiously, it was a degree of maturity well beyond her years. It became her strength.

From that moment on, she determined her life would be her responsibility because a surreal 'soul-destroying' experience was incomprehensible and after thirteen years of Catholic education. So, she contemplated, who would believe her? She knew her mother would, so she continued with their inner conversations. Violating her body and soul was not priestly. Least of all by a Jesuit. Purportedly, Father Thomas de Souza was the most Jesuitical of all Jesuits in Bahia.

Relieving herself of emotions, she believed the soul of her spirit was dying, but she thought of defiance. Arriving home late to be greeted by Dom Pedro's unmistakable booming voice echoing in the entrance hall, ricocheting with a call of displeasure. Undoubtedly, waiting to berate her recalcitrance with an overwhelming lashing tongue which would seal her fate. It dissolved her courage. Losing fate in her faith, Olga Sara desperately wanted to escape into the arms of her great aunt Emilia. Routinely busy at that time of day in the kitchen directing and cajoling cooks, preparing a Bahian dish with a variety of red meat, chilli and 'lashings of molasses' readied for a long slow cook. The cooks knew, just how the young Portuguese lady liked it.

A look of perturbation greeted the dishevelled state of 'her child' who would never leave home without being 'perfectly dressed for the occasion.' Emilia's sensitivity heightened as did her emotions. Perplexed, immersed in the smell of sweet and savoury ingredients, enveloped in an invisible mesh of tenderness, Emilia and Olga Sara arms wrapped around each other as tears streamed down to the blue patterned Portuguese tiles. Unnoticed, encased in the labyrinth of sensuality, they would have expected to hear the heavy boots that dare not enter the kitchen. Towering over them, with stunned cooks aghast, with one fell scoop Dom Pedro lifted them both unto the chez lounge in the anteroom for pre-dinner cocktails. Puzzled, but it was from habit.

Intermittently over a bowl of steaming soup mixed with her tears, Olga Sara confessed her crime of disobedience for the first time. She could not conceptualise her punishment but would accept it as she knew 'Jesus suffered more and for all of us.' Mesmerised, Emilia was stupefied accounting to Dom Pedro and assuming responsibility. After a quarter-century, he full well knew his wife's integrity of character. With two ladies sobbing uncontrollably in his arms, he was unbelievably silent but with penetrating lucidity he hatched a plan for what he declared was 'the work of the devil is the devil.'

Mute, a result of the senselessness of the crime, Dom Pedro left the belle epoque behind. Where to? They never knew, and he never said. Persisting for over half a century, and preserved by the cathedral, a copy of the meticulously recorded interview was finally read. Its style was credited to the inquisition which demanded 'accurate and careful documentation of any misdemeanour by the clergy.' Calling for a meeting of the Cathedral Committee, Father Thomas de Souza was suspended from all ecclesiastical duties and confined to the Presbytery. From weeks of self-imposed exile in her room consumed with shame and loathing, pregnancy was pronounced. Olga Sara was transported to a sanctuary of despondency and dejection.

Within a matter of weeks, the priest was brought from the desolation of confinement, where he was ostracised by all at the Presbytery, to testify before the tribunal comprised of every member of the Cathedral Committee. Police and military dossiers detailed a litany of misdemeanours, including proselytising communist ideology. Many were unsubstantiated as he followed the Jesuit avowed belief in social justice, which they referred to as liberation theology and the government described as communism. Paramount for Jesuits was education and educating workers about their rights was a priority as the majority had little formal education. References, including from the seminary in Goa, described him as 'an intelligent priest who cared deeply for his flock.'

Refusing representation, no support afforded by the ecclesiastical hierarchy for breaking the bonds of the Order. Ostracised, he was confronted with a conspiracy of silence in a climate of complicity. Presenting a picture of a lonely man adrift in a power structure searching for a lifeline to salvation, his interrogation lasted six hours and forty–five minutes.

Father Thomas de Souza's testimony was an epistle. Accepting responsibility and pleading guilty, in loneliness, praying in silence to his God for forgiveness. At the trial, he was fronted by twelve stony-faced men staring at him, indignant in a justification, elevated on a pedestal of moral and religious superiority. Sitting much lower, the soon to be defrocked priest opened with an epistemological treatise, which was only interrupted by Bishop Almeida to ensure accuracy for the record. Father de Souza recounted his experience serving the people of Bahia.

Complaints to superiors about the increasing poverty and its impact on children who grew up without fathers, some identified by priests but not acknowledged by uncaring plantation managers. Resulting in complainants, like himself, being isolated and confined to serving the plantations and seldom in the city. Astonishingly, it was not uncommon, as (*meia casta*), half-caste priests were not readily accepted by the European Brazilians, and indeed the presbyterate where they lived who fuelled the conspiracy.

Father de Souza reiterated the incident at the Fazenda on being castigated and humiliated by Senhora Dona Maria Camargo, the *Matrona,* for demanding that the *jovem* be allowed to meet the families, to which Olga Sara had agreed. Isolated from the reality of the plantations in Cidade Alta was an abrogation of their responsibility to God. Equating the young lady's cloistered upbringing to being a vestal virgin, exposed his animosity to the establishment families.

Olga Sara was received and treated reverently. In his many visits, Senhora Camargo never welcomed him to the Fazenda. Yet he was a messenger of God. Reluctance to revere him was based on her belief that God would not forgive her sins unless she confessed to a *superior caserdote Portugues.* Despite reporting to his superior, he had to continually endure her prejudicial opprobrium. On this matter the priest said in a similar vein, he was offended by the young Portuguese lady, who he referred to as Maria, insinuation that he was not Portuguese. For the first time, publicly invoking and resurrecting the pain he endured that plagued and epitomised his three years and nine months mission.

Poor parishioners, on the other hand, greeted and treated him with the reverence he was entitled to for spreading the word of God. Perhaps, the priest avers, it was the reason why he identified with them and empathised with their disadvantages which were not being addressed by the Church or governments. As a result, he predicted that it would lead to revolution, vilifying and castigating those who occupied the land for not observing the dictum of noblesse oblige: the principle that privilege did indeed entail responsibility.

Subscribing from its genesis to the philosophy advocated by Jesuits from the very few available pamphlets on liberation theology, Father de Souza detailed the influence it had on him. It led to his abhorrence of governments and elites, especially for equating it with communism, when it was in fact about social justice. Priests through spirituality and speaking mystically did not alleviate poverty and suffering. Advocating prayers and nonviolence, liberation theology aimed to eradicate poverty in Latin America and then the world. Making poverty history was Jesuitical.

Gazing defiantly at the committee as his testimony to the commission drew to a close, Father de Souza, *a pardo,* olive skin complexion with black lightly curly hair stretched himself beyond his small stature. He made it clear that the status quo preserved Brazil's institutional structures which perpetuated poverty and inequality. Persisting, it will disintegrate the largest country on the continent, which in 1957 was not inconceivable as there were eyewitnesses to repression. There were indeed many, he testified, with memories and evidence of violent suppression of slave revolts in the

Northeast persisting after abolition in 1888. Periodic incidents of riots and violence still occasionally erupted over poor people feeling disenfranchised. Summing up his assessment, he described the poor as suffering 'at the hands of devils.'

Inconceivable, but perception in the southern states and especially Sao Paulo, was that the Northeast was noticeably different from other parts of Brazil and should secede. Described as the 'Blackest State,' it was a result of what was the 'age of conquest' for these people and epitomised racism in Brazil. Bahia, known for slavery, sugar cane and carnival was no longer an asset. Rather it was a liability. Should succession from Brazil be openly discussed, it would not be resisted as there was no agreed narrative of a nation. Therefore, it was highly likely not to be resisted by a federal administration as it would be sponsored by the military.

Distilling the essence of the testimony of a man of mixed ancestry, who believed membership of the Society of Jesus was a certainty in elevating his status in a society mired in inequality was breathtaking in its audacity. A concatenation of incidents made him disdainful of the circumstances that relegated him to a state of rejection, but it gave him the latitude to express his true feelings wrapped in emotion. Father de Souza knew no other opportunity would have been afforded him.

Questioned, he did not identify the wealthy families, when asked, instead referred to them as an amorphous entity. Castigating the Church for its duplicity and complicity, Father de Souza praised the Order of the Society of Jesus as the beacon of enlightenment. Saying, he believed firmly it was the only hope for the Church as they wanted people to be educated so that they can read the Bible rather than having it interpreted for them. Peering from the past at the turn of events on Wednesday 13 March 2014 would have beguiled him. An Argentine, Jorge Mario Bergoglio, who supported liberation theology and was an advocate while bishop of Buenos Aires, was elected the first Jesuit Pope, celebrated by the Society of Jesus as its apotheosis.

Finally, there was a clarion call from Father de Souza, with a thinly veiled suggestion in his testimony 'of taking responsibility' implying that he could marry the young lady he 'blessed' with child. The cloaked reference was not acknowledged. But it was unimaginable contemplating a union with a man, fuelling conspiracy, and a decade and a half older. A man who was adversarial and determined not to succumb to the bullying and lambasted in mockery from arrogance of superiority. Offering, in his testimony, that left to their own device, authoritarian governments pursued policies that benefit the group with wealth through which they gain power and more wealth, leaving citizens with no power, receiving no benefits from their country's assets.

A unanimous decision described Father Thomas de Souza's actions as 'insidiously seditious' and recommended the harshest punishment: ex-communication and deportation. When the bishop, as chairman of the Cathedral

Committee, proclaimed that their recommendation was not binding, as the Vatican was the final arbiter, Dom Pedro, determined it an obstruction of natural justice and accused him of protecting the Diocese by evading scrutiny.

Instructing the military, the bishop intended to uncover any evidence of the teaching of liberation theology, allowing the armed forces to vindicate his Church in Bahia from accusations of propagating communism. Putting up a spirited fight, protecting his great-niece, Dom Pedro took the opportunity to remind the bishop that for centuries the de Oliveira Evora family had been a major benefactor of the cathedral. Other members contributed to a lesser extent, but they nevertheless fully supported Dom Pedro.

Knowing that the Vatican was mired in centuries of bureaucratic rituals, meaning decision making was a lengthy, slow and cumbersome, Dom Pedro recommended that his brother Dom Jose in Evora, the young lady's grandfather would discuss the sentence with the Portuguese Cardinal in Lisbon and escalate the matter to the Holy See. Lubricating the archaic medieval cloisters with donations from the young lady's inheritance unclogged the channel to excommunication.

According to the diocese records, Senhor Thomas de Souza resettled in Mozambique, then a Portuguese colony across the Atlantic from Bahia. Eighteen years after his banishment, Mozambique gained independence. Leading up to it the country witnessed periodic violent uprisings propelling the country into communism. Given the scale of destruction, colonial and Church records were comprehensively obliterated. Searching did not reveal any evidence of his presence in Maputo. Apparently, before the uprising, all the church records would have been sent to the Vatican. A trademark of the military for opponents was the concept euphemistically referred to as 'disappearance,' which effectively meant that a body had never been identified. International organisations' investigations of the Brazilian, Argentine and Chilean military regimes, specifically, uncovered atrocities recorded by Tribunals in the 1980s and 1990s. Dom Pedro was well placed to influence senior career officers, given his business and position on the Cathedral Committee. Unearthed was a tawdry tale that was to be marked 'not to be opened' by the Committee and none of the members disclosed its findings. Other Jesuits described him as characteristically enigmatic, highly intelligent, and epitomising the sanctity of the Order. Tormented from many years of subservience, Father Thomas de Souza was believed to have succumbed to 'a fit of pique.'

Radicalised by a coterie of Jesuits seeking and fomenting a solution to the rampant and unfettered accumulation of wealth at the expense of the poor, the doctrine of liberation theology came to be supported by members of other religious orders. With the tacit support of the Catholic Church these groups had been making representations to democratically elected governments, and military regimes to heed the needs of the poor, but with little success.

Alleviating poverty and in tandem social injustice were what the Catholic Church, professed to advocate in its mission and was supposedly its historical mandate from the teachings of the Bible. Widespread frustration led to the decision for a combined effort of the church in Latin America to join forces as poverty was endemic and the poor felt powerless and neglected by governments and the wealthy. In the movement's first officially sanctioned meeting in 1968, it stated that 'the situation of the poor demands all-embracing, courageous, urgent and profoundly renovating transformations.'

Believing that priests and nuns were conservative, governments on the continent were taken by surprise with their activism. Priests such as Brazilian Franciscan, Father Leonardo Boff, had been writing on these issues, making representations, and agitating about the state of the poor for many years. Pope Francis, a member of the Jesuits, was a Bishop in Buenos Aires during the development of liberation theology and advocated its aims. One of his predecessors, John Paul II gave legitimacy to liberation theology when he declared, 'Christian social doctrine was concerned with the human condition, freedom and dignity.'

Liberation theology grew rapidly, a result of the lack of action by Latin American governments of all persuasion. But governments, the military, elites, and big business described the doctrine as 'a dictum of Marx's philosophy of not to understand the world but to change it,' which resonated with sayings from the Old Testament. Liberation theology was taken from Christian theology and mixed with aspects of Marxism.

Clouded by historical distortions, Brazil's treatment of Amerindians and Africans, had to be the responsibly of the elites, military, and the Catholic Church. Catholic social ideology had traditionally articulated the danger of abuse of profit, but it had always recognised the legitimacy of business. The poor and powerless believed business was a contributor to poverty.

From experience, as a seventeen-year-old, Olga Sara developed an antipathy to the Catholic Church. Respecting liberation theology, however, she nevertheless abhorred Jesuits. Traumatic as it was, her ordeal became a recurring nightmare she endured throughout her life, which also elicited fear specifically during periods of stress. Although she lost 'her faith' she would, however, keep to and observe religious obligations. But she would 'never forgive or forget.' Perhaps, it contributed to, and became the harbinger for her pursuit of Judaism.

Back in Sao Paulo, a period of ambivalence incrementally evolved into acceptance of her fate as she resigned herself to it after her trauma. Failure of her monthly cycle changed her prognostications of a future immersed in creativity with the ambition of global proportions. Olga Sara found solace in isolation, dreaming of her mother, and seeing her in a divine apparition. Unflinching support came from great aunt Emilia who was her paragon. With the pregnancy confirmed, Dom Pedro acted without hesitation to minimise reputational damage to himself and the family. With the support of the Archbishop of Salvador, Olga Sara was to be moved to the convent and once the baby was born, arrangements had been made for the child to be adopted by a career military officer and Olga Sara sent to Evora to her grandparents.

Dom Pedro could never have envisaged the controversy that would erupt half a century later in Latin America and especially Argentina, resulting from the 'adoption' of babies of the opponents of military regime who disappeared. It became a common practice. A practice so callously executed, it led to a Commission of Inquiry to trace the biological parents of thousands of children who were adopted by career officers and their supporters. Dom Pedro's devious plan met with opprobrium by Emilia who without hesitation stymied it.

Olga Sara knew little about Joseph, except that he was a medical doctor from a mixed ancestry of Portuguese and Tupi Indian from Manaus. It came to her attention just before the wedding that he was approximately a decade older than her. Responding to resigning herself to life not as it was but what she could make it. She would as women in the de Oliveira Evora family had for centuries married older men. Purportedly, marrying young women in the prime of child-bearing age, was to ensure the preservation of their lineage preferably through sons. Resulting in generations of widowed women who became the purveyors of family history.

Unfortunately for the de Oliveira Evora family, the mythology did not dance to their tune. For them, the calamity and a contributor to unrealised ambition were that the only male child was illegitimate as was his mother. And both were not in clear Portuguese lineage. Olga Sara believed the dynasty could have been preserved as designed for centuries as her son went on to be a high achiever, not in a part of the far-flung empire but a dominion of the British Empire. Coincidentally it was just when the dynasty was teetering on the precipice of uncertainty.

It was an arranged marriage. Olga Sara knew that she had to accept what the family in Brazil and Portugal determined to be in her best interest. Following others' orders was what she had to subscribe to, which she confided in a treatise in her journal. Pouring her heart out, she eulogised her love as a sixteen-year-old for Parish, the brother of her school friend. Two years older than her, they decided to wait until she was eighteen when they could tell his parents and her guardians about their love.

Over months of the pregnancy, she was in a lamentable state of demoralisation struggling with abandonment, sometimes in stupefaction yet with penetrating lucidity she would wake enveloped in the fresh spring smell of Palheiro gardens. At times she was in an imagined reality of dreams as the music box played to her memories. She would come to keep her amulet under her pillow as it portends fleeting visions of her mother dressed in flowing white, gliding through Palheiro. Olga Sara's fatalistic conviction in interminable solitude was of unrealised concupiscence.

On that designated Sunday, Olga Sara readied herself for a marriage she was not prepared for and in circumstances, she had not anticipated. In preparation, she took it upon herself to learn more about Manaus, the capital of Amazonas state, in the northern region of the country built at the confluence of the Negro and Solimoes rivers. What most interested her was its beautiful *Teatro Amazonas,* Opera House, which she bookmarked to visit for performance and gaze on its renaissance revival architecture. The world's renowned building was constructed in 1896 at the height of the rubber boom,

Joseph dos Barros knew Dom Pedro as they both worked in the Amazon. Dom Pedro's family company, de Oliveira Evora, was building roads to make the region more accessible to supply services to Amerindian tribes, for mining exploration and to curtail the Tupamaros guerrillas. The Tupamaros were an urban movement that arranged strikes in Sao Paulo to disrupt business.

Guerrillas were also active in the Amazon jungle on the Brazil-Uruguay border, camouflaged by the area's dense canopy of rubber and *ungurahui* trees. Militarily resisting landowners and the armed forces for what they perceived as rapacious exploitation of the resources, which only benefitted the military and elites at the cost of displacing the poor. Elite families with an abundance of resources understandably managed the situation better in the city. The poor in the Amazon settlements where mineral resources were extracted were subject to regular harassment by the military and landowners' 'irregular forces.'

Confronting this environment became a regular feature for Dr Joseph dos Barros who completed his medical degree at the University of Sao Paulo. Passionate about the region and people, the Department of Health was just as eager for him to work in the Amazon basin on the anti-malaria program which the World Health Organisation, an agency of the United Nations, had been conducting in Latin America since the late 1940s. Joseph deliberately chose to work on malaria from experiences in Manaus where deaths from malaria were among the highest in the country.

Malaria is a mosquito-borne disease caused by a parasite spread by the vector of the Anopheles mosquito. Predominantly afflicting the poor, it was allegedly perpetuated by inequality in marginalised communities in the developing world. Anopheles was more virulent than other mosquitoes as it was also responsible for spreading elephantiasis: enlargement of a person's arms and legs. Malaria reportedly killed more people than any other disease in the world. So, the campaign took unprecedented action based on the WHO's examination of its global implications.

In his hometown of Manaus, Joseph witnessed the impact on families, especially the elderly and children who were more susceptible to being bitten by mosquitoes. Fumigation of dwellings was widely pursued. Uncontrolled, no one escaped exposure to the fumes. The method used to eradicate mosquitoes in the world was the wide-spread liberal spraying of DDT. Introducing netting to cover beds and hammocks supplemented the program but were impractical and induced claustrophobia in people sleeping in hammocks. The futility of its utility prevailed among Amerindians for many years.

As a medical doctor in this vast region, Joseph was responsible for not only the health of the people but also had to report to the government on the social conditions of the Amerindians. Reports identified his network to have included international agencies, Brazilian government services, the military, mining companies' executives, priests and nuns. Despite their obvious differences in age and social status, Dom Pedro and Joseph developed a cordial, but not what would have been considered a close personal relationship. Joseph would occasionally be invited to dinner parties at Casa das Flores. He certainly saw Dom Pedro's children, as Olga Sara was assumed to be, and not dispelled by the family. She, however, did not recall him, though he would not have failed to notice an attractive vivacious teenager playing the piano at dinner parties; but never at fiestas which were the purview of men playing the guitars and Atabaque drums.

Joseph was undoubtedly aspirational. Of average height with olive complexion, lightly curly black hair and brown eyes, his attire was commented on for its sartorial elegance. When in Sao Paulo he wore off-white suits and a Panama hat in the summer and in winter Argentine blue woollen suits, always with matching tie and pocket kerchief emblazoned with an eponymous monogram in the breast pocket of his jackets. In the city, he always wore two-toned brogues, white with either brown or black.

Punctilious, Dom Pedro thought he seemed to be seeking perfection; reasons enough, he told Emilia, for him to be asked to marry Olga Sara. Joseph's wife died in childbirth. Discussions about him not socialising in Sao Paulo did not go unnoticed and was measured by the sheer number of dinner invitations he declined.

According to his colleagues, he sublimated his life into work on the death of his wife. Entrenchment in work was also a result of his growing concerns about the liberal spraying of DDT which may have been having deleterious effects on the Amerindians. Knowing Joseph's work practices, Dom Pedro believed those stories. But he knew from experience that as Joseph was aspirational he needed to develop networks in government and in the commercial community in Sao Paulo to be successful in his advocacy.

To assist, but unbeknown to him, Dom Pedro nominated Joseph for membership of the Grand Lodge of the Freemasons. Since its foundation, all the de Oliveira Evora men were Freemasons and Joseph was nominally considered as 'Evora' qualified. Credited to have been introduced to Portugal by English Protestant merchants in 1727, it experienced a turbulent period in its gestation in the staunchly Catholic country. Influenced by merchants, noblemen and members of the landed gentry who lobbied for positions of Grand Masters, it gained legitimacy. Popes issued Bulls (decrees) threatening members with excommunication. There is no evidence of sanction. It was thought that its popularity with men of the European establishment gave rise to the belief that its origins were influenced by the Knights Templar.

Freemasonry was introduced to Brazil when the Monarchy relocated from Portugal during the Napoleonic wars. By 1813 it had taken root in the state of Bahia followed by Rio de Janeiro and Sao Paulo. Membership was exclusively landowners, businessmen, and military officers. Several presidents of military regimes were Freemasons. Mired in controversy wherever they established Masonic Lodges, many Freemasons encountered criticism. To legitimise the organisation, reference was made to its influence on the United States constitution. And to the fact that its first president, George Washington, was a Freemason who was pictured wearing the Grand Master regalia. Proud to display his affiliation and allegiance, as the Freemasons were credited as the key network in the American Revolution.

In Brazil, Freemasons came to enjoy wide support for their role in the country's independence and the abolition of slavery. But criticised for their role in the expulsion of the Jesuits following the orders of the Marquis of Pombal, who administered the Empire from 1760 -1770. He ordered that the Jesuits' assets be made available to the Freemasons. President Salazar, however, ordered their abolition in

Portugal. Judging by the grandeur of their Grand Temple in places such as Sao Paulo, it was clear that Brazil ignored the Portuguese President's example.

From personal experience, Dom Pedro knew that as a Freemason, Joseph would have an avenue to express his frustrations over the 'Amerindian cause,' as it was commonly described, which would make its way to the hierarchy of the health department. Which means he would 'get the ear' of senior government officials, as most were Freemasons. From Olga Sara's journal, there was no evidence that Joseph ever became a Freemason. There were no rings with the insignia or photographs of him in ceremonial regalia as there was for other male members of the family, except Dom Pedro's younger brother, Alfonso. Speculation was that Father Bridges and Alfonso would have persuaded him otherwise. Whatever or whoever influenced his decision, Joseph was nevertheless still able to have an impact on curtailing the liberal spraying of DDT in the Amerindian villages. By the mid-nineteen sixties, DDT was more selectively sprayed.

Amerindians predominantly lived close to a network of multiple rivers crisscrossing the Amazon basin, from which they collected potable water. Their children played in the stagnant pools on which DDT was sprayed. Joseph identification with Amerindians was viewed dimly by departmental officials. Therefore, many of his reports received scant attention. One example was his recommendation for schools to increase the level of education so that villagers would be educated and learn to accept the utility of WHO programs, which he argued, would contribute to the organisation achieving its objectives.

Joseph was acknowledged by his contemporaries to have accurately reported what he observed in his extensive travel in Brazil, other Latin American countries, and the Caribbean. Reports were that the program was successful in high socioeconomic areas in these countries but unsuccessful in less developed areas. Unsurprisingly, it was later reported that these areas lacked the infrastructure, skilled technicians and managers needed to coordinate the program as there was a lack of support at the national level. The Amazon basin lacked all these prerequisites. Moreover, Joseph's disillusion with the program was possibly also influenced by American scientist Rachael Carson's book, *Silent Spring.*

Published in 1962, it stated that, 'DDT, the synthetic organic compound used as an insecticide, which has a deleterious effect on vertebrates was ineffective in the eradication of malaria.' Simultaneously, articles were being published in international journals about the harmful effects of DDT on communities where it was sprayed uncontrolled or used in other forms such as powder and paint. Vilified and ostracised, Carson did not live to witness the development of the environmental movement which she has been credited with creating.

What was revealed in the mid-1990s after Joseph's death, when a photograph with a plaque was exhibited in his memory in the board room of the Health Department in Sao Paulo, was that he was often present and unprotected, as were the workers. The procedure was to mix the powder with water to spray or paint walls in homes and community halls. Speculation remains over the cause of his untimely death.

Before the wedding, Emilia told Olga Sara that her grandparents would not be attending. Neither were surprised as they only visited once in Madeira but never came to see her in Sao Paulo. No reason was ever stipulated. What was uncovered, to her chagrin, was that her grandparents' visit to Madeira was to arrange for her mother to marry Manuel Goncalves. She imagined her mother would have rejected the proposition. Although they were not attending the wedding, they bequeathed her something from the family heirloom. At that moment, Olga Sara said she decided to never visit Portugal. She was also not to find out for many years about the inheritance which was given to Joseph as a *dote* (dowry).

Illegitimacy of birth negated the legitimacy of inheritance, according to Portuguese law. In the bewilderment of her bereavement for Lia Maria, Yolanda at an advanced age had appealed for guardianship of Olga Sara. Astonished at the reasons conjured up for its rejection, she waged a battle with her husband and sons not to succumb to the law, and to endow the child with a substantial inheritance to secure her from an uncertain fate. Using it as a dowry, Dom Pedro must have determined that he was executing the mandate of the inheritance, as he was her guardian.

The dowry was a European institution which continued to be practised by wealthy Portuguese in Brazil. Historical precedents turned it into a convention and advocated that it was the duty of a father to give a daughter a dowry on marriage. The dowry allowed wives to be financially independent and, also to assist a husband to provide for his wife as she had been accustomed. Wives were generally involved in their husband's business as it was a family enterprise and the reason for generations they were established as corporate entities. Marriage was therefore undoubtedly an economic arrangement and on occasion reverberated with social status symbolism.

There were no established criteria for what constituted a dowry and indeed its monetary value. It was a matter to be determined between the father or guardian and prospective husband. In the early period of settlement of the colonies, it consisted of land, houses, animals, and slaves. The type of dowry also demarcated social class. The elites who were Portuguese settlers and or were new arrivals from Portugal continued the practice until the mid-twentieth century. The dowry was neither practised by mestizo, descendants of intermarriage with Amerindians, nor by the lower classes who were Amerindians and Africans and classified in that order in Brazil.

What Olga Sara did not know, but would come to learn, epitomised Dom Pedro's absolute control in determining the course of her life. When he was ill, he sought forgiveness and reconciliation. Given what became known about their relationship, it was always deemed irreconcilable. When the decision was made to move her to Sao Paulo on her mother's disappearance, her grandparents established a trust fund for her with Dom Pedro as executor. Following tradition, she was not to get access to her inheritance until her twenty-first birthday in December 1961. This matter was never disclosed. Marrying at eighteen did not entitle her to the inheritance. Olga Sara always wondered whether the dowry may have been a decisive factor in Joseph's decision to proceed with marrying a pregnant teenager. Therefore, from her perspective, as she wrote, it may simply have been a marriage of convenience for Joseph.

The prevailing opinion, however, was that for Joseph, the marriage was indeed a commercial arrangement. Olga Sara, on the other hand, had already withdrawn from society, except for attendance at mass and other church activities. It's unimaginable how two people who were inseparable and shared much in common could become even closer given the relationship they developed since their Funchal to Sao Paulo journey a decade earlier. But by then her cousins had moved to college in Miami and Emilia devoted her life to the person she knew who most needed her but would never seek it.

Joseph's parents who lived in Manaus only met Olga Sara at her wedding and were reportedly disinterested in her and her son and developed a passive-aggressive approach to Dom Pedro. Publicly declaring they had no reason to visit Sao Paulo. It did not come as a surprise, as neither

Joseph nor his younger brother Vincente visited Manaus. It was surmised to be because they were both away from Sao Paulo most of the year. The reasons, however, were multifaceted. Revealing snippets from over half a century of early family oral history, it was a result of an unaccepted mixed marriage, and the couple eloping resulting in the boys enduring prejudice. Not surprising Brazil is still entangled in a web of prejudice.

On the eve of her wedding, Olga Sara repaired to bed early and indulged in speculating on her plans. In her journal, imaging she was being 'watched over' by a silhouette of her mother. Olga Sara's priority was not her impending marriage but a six-month-old son, a constant reminder of an unexpected life she did not choose. And here she was again without the opportunity to determine her future. Guilt-ridden she sublimated her love for her son. Her attention was liberally and unreservedly for him as she would not have chosen the journey she was about to embark on.

An expression of her love was detailed in her journal on the acquisition of an original copy of the *Missa Luba* to be given to him when he was older. It was well known in the Catholic community but was not officially recorded until 1964, despite having been performed in some European countries for several years. A version of the mass in Latin, it was composed by a Franciscan monk, Father Guido Haazen, in the Democratic Republic of Congo. It remained her son's favourite composition, holding a special place in his heart.

Marriage certainly did not interrupt Emilia and Olga Sara's *'tete-a-tete'*, both now more in need of each other, it appears. Emilia surmised that it was a loveless marriage, as Joseph's appearance at home became more irregular as he sublimated his life into his work. Allegedly, he took a public stance against the governments' policy over the spraying of DDT and privately sent reports to the WHO. Intentionally, it was to lead to investigations into the misallocation of United Nations funding of its program.

Funds allocated for malaria projects, he claimed, were being diverted for other purposes prescribed by 'vested interests.' Undoubtedly, to career military officers and their cohorts. It was claimed Joseph was alluding to corruption. Dom Pedro vociferously warned him to refrain from making public statements because of its implications for the family. Corruption was widespread under military regimes and Joseph was alerted to the diversion of funds allocated to Amerindian health and education which he intended to stymie.

Unrelieved and unmanageable frustrations apparently led Joseph to spend most of the first two years of marriage in the Amazon basin. Whether a result of a combination of work and unresolved domestic matters, he nevertheless retreated seeking comfort from excess drinking which he had not done prior to marriage. The abuse of alcohol by workers in remote areas was accredited to the nature of their work. Allegedly, alcohol anaesthetised their exposure to DDT, compounded by long periods away from their family.

Another unintended consequence which received little attention was co-habitation with Amerindian women. An increasing and unrecognised population of mixed-race children was hidden in the Amazon. Most of these illegitimate children were not recognised by any official authority or their father's families. From all accounts, Joseph was a 'happy drunk.' Disinhibited, he would sing an English ditty popular in the music halls in the 1920s, 'I'm forever blowing bubbles, pretty bubbles…' Alcohol abuse became contentious in the family especially with his brother Vincente who Olga Sara confided in about her challenges.

Increasingly concerned about her marriage and embarrassed by Joseph's abuse of alcohol, she confided in Emilia on matrimonial matters too. Emilia reverted to what was a common solution, sharing marital woes with their parish priest. Recommending Father Fernando Moreira, with whom Olga Sara had developed a cordial, but ambivalent relationship, as it was with all Jesuits, was therefore expected. Cognisant of her antipathy towards Jesuits, however, the priest saw it as his duty to seek the counsel of Dom Pedro before his audience with Dr Joseph dos Barros.

Approximately six months later, when Olga Sara had given up hope of being assisted to find a solution to her marital woes, as prayers did not, her spirits lifted. Father Moreira told her after the regular Sunday morning mass that he would like to visit her at home. Given her predicament, she would not acquiesce. Meeting alone, despite the presence of maids in the home, reverberated with fear resulting in her feeling nauseous for several days.

Increasingly depending and being concerned about her dependency, which she expressed in her journal, Olga Sara resorted to Emilia's counsel. Responding crisply 'leave it to me,' which she willingly wanted to do. She requested that Dom Pedro was not to be made aware of the situation, as it would compound and complicate her fear. Scheduled for that Tuesday at Casa das Flores, it was opportune as it coincided with Olga Sara's increasingly frequent visits and with the certainty of the absence of her great uncle.

On finding his way through the labyrinth, as the mansions were expanding at an unprecedented rate, to Casa das Flores, Father Moeira promptly expressed disappointment at Dom Pedro's absence. But succumbed, as he was flushed with expectations and delighted to settle for coffee and Portuguese tart. It was obvious that despite Olga Sara feeling at twenty-one, she was now entitled to determine what she wanted to do and make decisions for herself. Church and societal etiquette, however, imposed standards which were not in keeping with her expectations. Irritated, she nevertheless acquiesced at not being required to participate in a meeting where she was a significant actor. Bowing to Emilia's wishes, however, as her agitation reached heights of distress, Olga Sara and her son walked the gardens, allowing for him to kick the autumn leaves while she admired the golden leaves of the Japanese maples and golden Elms which were planted on the estate, as a result of her influence.

With her great aunt approaching wearing a sombre face, Olga Sara's heart sank; despair was again her companion. Emilia, also an actively keen gardener, walked with her as the reluctant child was flittered away. Without exchanging a glance or 'so much as a word,' according to Olga Sara journal entry, Emilia observed her anxiety and emerging tears. Silently sitting on the bench, Emilia had designed for her new garden, early in her marriage. It was built by the quiet handyman from brazilwood in an ornate style with metal club feet and a curvaceous armrest. Olga Sara leaned forward putting her face in her hands to hold back the tears in transit, to flow unobstructed when Emilia held her tightly. Their emotions merged as their heartbeat synchronised. They were at one in the divine spirit.

Eloquently delivered with reverence and supreme tenderness, the intimate conversation took its natural course. More correctly, the instructions Father Moreira imparted in solemnity were delivered to Olga Sara clearly and concisely but reassuringly empathic. In unison, the ladies sheathed home the responsibility for their predicament to Dom Pedro. For Emilia, it was Olga Sara's 'cri de coeur.' For her, it was Santo Emilia's apparition as her guardian angel.

Emilia Alves del Castillo de Oliveira Evora was a strikingly attractive woman of medium height, slim build with auburn hair and smiling green eyes. With a Romanesque chiselled nose, she carried herself with an air of distinction with irresistible charm and a gentle manner. Some equated her style as 'arrogance.' With a mellifluous voice, she spoke in measured tones. European educated, fluent in several languages, she was continuously resplendent. Under guardianship, she became Olga Sara's de facto mother giving love unflinching, imparted with great compassion.

Delivering the eulogy, Olga Sara described Emilia, as 'always acting with the utmost dignity and decorum.' Emilia was from Argentina. Her parents Antonio and Consuela Alves del Castillo came from Mendoza, the country's second-largest city, renowned for fine wine. Its natural beauty accentuated by its position on the eastern side of the Andes, towered over by snow-capped Mount Aconcagua, the highest peak in the western hemisphere.

General Antonio del Castillo served as a Defence *Attache* in Paris and Madrid. And was posted as a ministerial adviser in London and Washington to Argentinian military regimes, including during the presidency of Juan Domingo Peron in the 1950s. In this position, he was a member of the embassy and the government's entourage during the president and his wife, Evita Duarte Peron's, European visits. A career military officer, undoubtedly trained in intelligence, sworn to secrecy, he would never deconstruct the entrails of the Peronist era Argentina still struggles with. Though he professed on retirement in Madrid that he had not been a Peronist.

The General was a witness to major political upheaval in Argentina and contributed to government policy during the era of two of his most famous compatriots, Evita, and

Ernesto 'Che' Guevara. Although she spent little time in Buenos Aires since marrying, Emilia was a frequent visitor and took 'the girls' with her to appreciate the country she loved, given Adelia and Estrelle's Portuguese and Argentinian ancestry. A later addition, Olga Sara nevertheless equalled them in the adulation of Buenos Aires, a city of great architectural beauty on the western shore of the estuary of the *Rio de la Plata* (River Plate.) Emilia professed her love for the city which was more than she had done for Sao Paulo.

The del Castillo's Buenos Aires residence in the grand old Villanueva mansion between Avenida Cordoba and Avenida Corrientes was in the heart of the city. The home was close to the Obelisk with commanding views of the city and marks the area where the country was settled. Clearly, an inheritance, it was in an ideal location from where it was conducive to promenading the wide avenues. Also, facilitating visits to some of the many monuments and grand buildings of the most European of all South American cities. Emilia took the liberty of showing the girls places made famous by Evita, where she was renowned for purportedly working for the poor who she called '*descamisados*' (shirtless ones.)

Emilia, like most *Portinos*, emulated Evita as she was a purveyor of fashion and remained their role model even after death. Evita died in 1952 creating an outpouring of grief, the magnitude of which was never to be seen again in Latin America. Grieving for Evita was not an indulgence of

Emilia's grandmother, who was permanently at home in her mansion. Her family and Aurelia Tizon Peron, Juan Peron's first wife, were cousins. The girls remembered 'their great grandmother' Luisana with warmth and loved her dearly, even though they had difficulty understanding her dulcet tones as she spoke a mixture of her native Italian and Argentine Spanish. Purposely or inadvertently these three young ladies were vicariously imbued with an enduring love of Buenos Aires. None more so than the latecomer, who retrospectively discerned memories of another time and place and tried to counter them with regular visits with two of her children to places for the memory of 'a time and a place.'

Known for giving extravagantly, yet unprepared to express an opinion on Che, General de Castillo was a dilettante of Formula One motor racing. In reverent tones, he would speak about another famous countryman, Juan Manuel Fangio, who had again won the championship in 1957. Fangio dominated the first decade of the sport by winning five championships, a record unbroken for half a century. Proudly claiming his influence may have sparked Carlos' interest when he commenced his apprenticeship in motor racing at Brands Hatch. With his credentials and prowess confirmed, instructor Tony Lanfranchini also took to calling him 'Fangio.' Enthusiastically introducing another South American to James Hunt in 1975, the year before he won the World Championship. Reference to him as Fangio was the pretext for him to make another pilgrimage with his mother to Buenos Aires.

On acquiring a greater understanding of Che Guevara, Olga Sara would come to respect what he wanted to achieve, observing the growth of inequality and disparity in wealth in what the family referred to as the twin cities of Buenos Aires and Sao Paulo. Guevara's philosophy and plans were for Latin America to adapt the policies he helped develop which was to be instituted in Cuba after the 1959 revolution. Fidel Castro's guerrillas overthrew the US-backed dictatorship of military sergeant Fulgencio Batista. Latin American military regimes were determined that he not be allowed to propagate his philosophy in any other country to the Argentine revolutionary. A policy avidly supported by the administration in the United States. Che failed before he got started in South America. Hunted down and killed by US and Bolivian soldiers in 1967 before he could launch his ill-prepared attempt to spread his message of social justice.

Olga Sara and Emilia sitting close and looking inseparable, now with more in common, on their favourite garden bench. With the responsible gardener, Mendes, they were creating a garden on the rolling grasslands which ambitiously was copied as a scaled-down version of Palheiro, to be named Lia Maria's Jardim. Emilia looked into Olga Sara's eyes, taking her hands and in saintly patience said, 'my child, your mother would be proud to see the beautiful young lady you turn out to be, intelligent, highly capable of achieving what you want and admired by all who know you, none more so than me and aunty Bea.'

Emilia, tears welling, reflectively spoke openly for the first time on a most personal of matters. 'You know, when I saw you standing with Sister Francis at the door of the convent, I hugged you loving you with all my heart.' What I saw was a child waiting for someone who we knew may not be returning. That is when I looked at you and thought I would now have a child of my own who I could share my life with as you now do with your son.'

Baffled, Olga Sara said, questioning, 'but you have your daughters, Adelia and Estrelle. Prevaricating, carefully considering her position, quietly speaking in those mellifluous tones, 'Ours is a conspiracy of secrecy which made sense.' Seemingly in readiness, confidently, Emilia recounted how she met Dom Pedro, a tall dashing, self-confident man who her father said was assisting with developing roads into the Amazon. Reporting that he was highly thought of by the government, career military officers and the Church. Meeting her father's criteria of a husband.

Within twelve months, they had a splendid society wedding attended by government officials, diplomats, generals, and the archbishop of Sao Paulo. 'Your grandparents came from Evora as did family members from Madeira. We returned with them to spend our honeymoon in Europe. I wanted to show Dom Pedro Paris and Rome. We went to England to see Alfonso.

I had always wanted to return and visit some of the famous English gardens such as Kew Gardens. For Emilia, the most beautiful garden in England was Sissinghurst

Castle in Kent, hosting an exceptionally beautiful home and garden 'that inspired me when I was designing our garden.' Developed by Vita Sackville-West, a poet, and her husband, Harold Nicolson, a diplomat, who had worked with her father. Emilia declared it was where she had the idea to plant golden elms, 'under which we now sit.' Here we can admire the radiant autumn colours. 'You will agree it was a good decision.' Smiling in acquiescence, Olga Sara delivered her opinion too. Emilia said, 'you must go there sometime.' With great flourish, sketches of Sissinghurst would appear in her journal direct from Emilia's photographs and bring to life by annotations in the margins.

Emilia explaining that when her father was posted to London as a defence attache, he worked with and befriended Harold Nicholson, who managed extensive holdings in Argentina, which included railways, industries, and even polo clubs, where they both played. Harold Nicholson and his wife Vita Sackville-West designed and developed the castle in the 1930s. Incidentally, it was used during the war as a hospital.

Defiantly expressive, Emilia teasingly told her that there was 'much you should know and there is much you have to do. Like you, Adelia and Estrelle turned out to be beautiful and accomplished young ladies. I am proud of all of you.' Holding her breath, as if she was about to dive into the pool to demonstrate to the girls the qualities of a good swimmer, *'but none of you are my children.'* Although she looked askance, Olga Sara was not surprised at what Emilia then said, 'they are aunty Bea's daughters.'

Knowingly impatient, Dom Pedro was always a man in a hurry. There is much he wanted to achieve and having a family was a priority which we discussed in Lisbon as we walked along *Rio Tejo*. He recounted his childhood in Portugal and visits to his grandparents in Restelo, looking at ships moored, ready to sail to Brazil. Anxious to see places that were part of the Empire, he also wanted sons to continue the family business as his father and his brothers had done.

'Not for the want of trying' Emilia said, 'but I could not conceive and the many doctors' appointments in Sao Paulo, Buenos Aires and Europe offered little that would assist. Childless, Dom Pedro became preoccupied with his work and was away from home for long periods. 'That was just like your situation.' Then, 'I so remember, on a winter's evening, he rang to tell me he was bringing his office manager to have dinner with us. As you know, that is not surprising as he regularly invites people for meals without telling me or the cook. Yet expecting us to conjure up meals as desired. There and then I met Beatrice (Bea), Cordeiro. I had an epiphany. It explained his assignations.'

Within six months, Bea moved in with us to work on the design of infrastructure projects for the Amazon basin. 'I discussed the situation with my parents, but they paid little attention to my misgivings and my father said that I should refrain from expressing any concerns. When he agreed that we should, it was approaching our fifth wedding anniversary. Then Dom Pedro told me that Bea was pregnant. It was the most devastating and tumultuous period of my life. Shamed into embarrassment, it disrupted our plans, we did not return to Europe and it meant that we had to make significant changes to our lives. That was when my father took a different perspective and discussed the situation with the bishop of Mendoza.

The advice he received, was exactly what Father Moreira said, I should tell you and that we should discuss the matter with Dom Pedro: apply for an annulment of the marriage.' From the perspective of the Catholic Church, a husband or wife can apply for an annulment which implies that the marriage was invalid or had not been consummated, and in keeping faithful to the teachings of the Church, salvation was being sought.

Commencing with interviews by the ecclesiastical delegates, submitting reports and evidence to the Papal Council in the Vatican, the process can be onerous and cumbersome and can take many months and even years. Once proven, the Church declares that a marriage is not for life and is annulled. 'That's it,' avers Emilia. Faithful to the wishes of the Church or blind fate? Intellectually sophisticated, with a lifetime of education in catholic institutions, but with exposure to the hypocrisy of monumental proportions, she refrained from blasphemy.

Ingenious in solemnity, cautiously delivering her assessment, Emilia did indeed not want to purposely influence a fragile and impressionable young lady. Voicing repressed and undoubtedly sublimated anxieties with the confidence of her indignation with this irremediable fact. Emilia postulated a proposition on the infallibility of the Pope. Concluding 'everyone is a sinner,' which was the purpose of redemption. Incrementally, growing to distrust priests, she questioned the need for an intermediary to God. Given their emotional connectivity, Olga Sara intuitively grasped the implications and spontaneously made the sign of the cross and bowed her head in the silence of oblivion.

Fortuitously, it brought to her realisation Emilia's prognostications about her ambivalence to the paintings and life of Spain's most famous seventeenth-century painter, Francisco de Jose Goya, who she greatly admired. Goya also had a complicated relationship with the Church as his paintings vividly demonstrate. His most famous painting sent a message to the Church: 'Let there be light.'

Contemplating the consequences, Emilia's gentle caress was not of the timbre she had ever received. It was, in fact, a loving embrace that put Olga Sara into a trance like state, reminiscent of the love from her mother. Emilia said, 'It was a lamentable situation. Poor child, you did not even have the white wedding you wanted. My dear Olga Sara, you now see the predicament we are both in and I was not allowed to proceed, but instead, it was my cross to bear, though it turned out not to be because I was expected to be a mother.' Once Bea gave birth to the girls, she was more interested in returning to work to be with Dom Pedro, clearly indicating she had no interest in motherhood. Caring and loving them unreservedly is why they call me mother and they call her 'aunty Bea.'

Astonishingly, telling the girls was not a traumatic experience as had been anticipated. It was not until they were sixteen and eighteen that Dom Pedro, Emilia, and Beatrice told Adelia and Estrelle that Bea was their mother. Famously as expected, they expressed great consternation in the emotionally charged atmosphere. 'Which I was left to manage.' After a brief hiatus as they resigned into resolution, they continued to call me '*mae.*' Yet, Olga Sara said, 'Dom Pedro always seeks your opinion and advice on family and business matters and you also attend social functions, while Bea stays in the background.'

Compromising to accommodate each other was how they managed their private and public lives. Incidentally, this matter was never again discussed, but she shared it with her daughter Carmelita. True to form, it did not appear in any of the women's journals. What was, however, written was thought to be either from what Emilia may have said or Olga Sara had surmised. 'The saint pays for the sinner.' Emilia knew that Dom Pedro, his father, and brothers were bitterly disappointed as none of them fathered sons, unlike their father. Devastated, their desire to continue a dynasty was unlikely to be realised. Alluded to, many times throughout the centuries, speculation on what could have been was also evidently imagined.

According to Emilia, Beatrice Cordeiro's ancestors were North African Moors from Portugal. They converted to Christianity and migrated to Brazil where they reverted to practising the Islamic faith. Bea, however, had no religious affiliation and never expressed interest in Islam or Catholicism. Dom Pedro engaged her on a project when she was eighteen and living in Salvador. He knew little about her family and she volunteered little. Apparently, she was estranged from them and that was why she left to 'make her way in the world.' They have never met or has anyone visited her family who lived near Salvador. 'We are a Catholic family' Emilia said, 'so I arranged the girls' baptism and communion at the cathedral.'

Olga Sara felt like Emilia, she was in a quandary and now the matter had to be left to divine providence. Annulment was therefore never mentioned, remaining a secret between the women and a priest. Although it warranted confession, she was assured by Emilia that Father Moreira treated this matter like he would a confession. She did not record the penance and absolution in her journal.

Ever since she was a child of seven, the only person Olga Sara trusted was great aunt Emilia. That feeling was reaffirmed when she hugged and kissed her on both cheeks, took her hands and told her they had to find a solution. And despite fearing Dom Pedro, Olga Sara had to let him sort out the reasons for Joseph's extended absence from home. Keeping her commitment, Emilia designed a solution and Olga Sara willingly acquiesced. They entered Casa das Flores from the garden as a housemaid held the door and Erminia, ran to greet them, and said she was cooking Olga Sara's favourite dish. The Portuguese lady never told anyone that she did not eat dishes containing molasses.

Three months later when Joseph returned home to Jardim Europa, Olga Sara and Carlos were still in residence at Casa das Flores. During this period, she had taken to assist in the garden, freely playing piano compositions of Eric Sate and George Gershwin. And taking the opportunity to show the variety of music she had been introduced to by Joseph, playing the music from the guitars of *Los Indios Tabajaras,* especially Maria Elena. Composed and played by two Amerindian brothers from Ceara State, Northeast Brazil, it was her husband's favourite music. The women rekindled their love of literature and poetry. Reverting to the poetry of Jose Marti, and Neruda. And re-reading the books of their favourite authors, Tolstoy, and Dostoyevsky. Unsurprisingly, these were books, Olga Sara's mother and great grandmother Yolanda also loved and highly recommended.

A common perception was Latin American men have mistresses. Well, known authors from the continent including Gabriel Garcia Marquez wrote about this subject and its effect on families when children's biological fathers are not uncovered. Suffering the indignity and prejudice, many street children in Sao Paulo are a result of this phenomenon. A common belief prevailed that military officers and wealthy men went to church with their wives and fiestas with their mistresses. Men working in the Amazon away from home were more prone to fathering children out of wedlock. There was an unwritten code, literally translated meaning, 'what happens in the Amazon stays in the Amazon.' Doubts were cast over Joseph as it did with Dom Pedro. Both men took their wives to church and social activities.

Joseph and Dom Pedro agreed that Olga Sara must return to their home as soon as his brother from England had an opportunity to spend time getting to know her and Carlos. Emilia was preparing Olga Sara to meet her uncle. Expecting that he would be like his brother, she was petrified and was eager to return home to Joseph. On meeting great uncle Dom Alfonso with his daughter Penelope, Olga Sara was visibly nervous. Proud of her multilingualism which failed her, as did her prognostication, she was overcome by his warmth and humanity. She burst into tears. Embarrassed, she rushed out of the family room as Carlos too ran and cried in fear. Alfonso knelt and picked up the child before Emilia could, as Penny came into the room.

'Precisely at that moment and with that gesture,' Olga Sara pencilled briskly in her journal, 'I knew I had found someone who, like Emilia, would be my saving grace.' With Emilia's indulgence, Alfonso and Olga Sara spent time together talking in the garden as Penny was taken sightseeing in the state by Adelia home from Miami. where she went to study and decided to stay. Her sister was also in the US and still at college.

Most wealthy families sent their children to the US or Europe to be educated. That practice became prevalent during periods of military regimes, as the universities and especially Sao Paulo's, were described as a 'hotbed of radicals.' Officers attended university and were considered middle class. Soldiers were lower class. Directed by officers, who disliked the self-indulgence of privileged students, soldiers were given carte blanche to 'dish out' punishment when there were anti-regime demonstrations.

Alfonso and Penny met Joseph when he came to visit before leaving for Cuba where the World Health Organisation was also conducting a malaria eradication program, which meant he was not expected back in Sao Paulo for a month. The arrangement was that Olga Sara would be returning home before him getting back from Cuba. She confided that she was now more prepared and was committed to use her great aunt as her model and make her marriage a success.

Alfonso was an inspiration and extravagantly generous. He encouraged his great niece to give the marriage her 'best shot.' Olga Sara was feeling that by the time he and Penny left Sao Paulo, she and Carlos would be more attuned to English habits, such as marmalade at breakfast, and the singing of ditties such as 'he's a jolly good fellow,' which he and Penny regularly sang with Carlos who eagerly recited it to visitors.

Their presence, affability, and attention given to Carlos was incrementally contributing to the improvement in his behaviour. On many occasions, Olga Sara confided in her journal and inadvertently documented the transformation in her son's behaviour. Half a century later reading what his mother wrote about him was cathartic. For her, he was a 'difficult child.' 'I am not sure what to do with him?' 'What will become of him?' On one of his many tantrums, she wrote, soon after returning home from Casa das Flores, and in the presence of Alfonso, Carlos, seeking attention kicking and screaming, 'I am a warrior!' before his mother could give him the attention he craved. Nurturing him was her only means of protecting her fatherless child from what she did not know. Picking up the screaming child, Alfonso declared, 'you are a warrior, my boy.'

Olga Sara, for the first time in her short relationship with Alfonso, unapologetically took the child to protect him from what she knew. 'Don't tell him that. Uncle Dom Pedro always calls him our little warrior when he misbehaves and that is why I do not like him spending time there. Trembling, she declared, 'I know he does not like Carlos.' Olga Sara preferred Emilia comforting him with empathy, compassion, love, and gentleness.

Planting kisses on his forehead, she called him, 'Che.' Startling herself, Emilia had revealed one of her best kept secrets. Carlos, many years later remembering those precious moments would call her 'Santo Emilia.' It was just another family secret for Carlos to uncover which was stupendously revelatory.

Che was popularised by the Argentinian revolutionary Ernesto Guevara and mythologised by his followers in Cuba and indeed globally. It, however, was an honorific used for men from Argentina. Of all members of the family,

Emilia was entitled to call Carlos by that nom de plume as she changed the course of his life. She had arranged for his birth in Buenos Aires, as once Olga Sara's pregnancy became visible, Dom Pedro did not want her in Casa das Flores. Emilia implored her parents to rescue the pregnant teenager. Olga Sara remained in Buenos Aires for six months after giving birth, returning to Sao Paulo about three months before her wedding.

Alfonso was upset by Olga Sara's reaction when he called her son a little warrior. It had more to do, it was surmised with the comparison drawn with his brother. Regretting her outburst, she wrote, it was a multiplicity of factors. Visibly agitated and anxious, his stated reason was that Penny was later than expected in a period where kidnapping of children from wealthy families was a source of revenue for terrorists. Alfonso sat in the comfortable leather armchair and looking at the garden through the open French doors, said to Olga Sara, 'What Dom Pedro says to the boy is true.' Puzzled, she was about to ask him to explain, which is exactly what he was about to do. He told her that the family does not talk about its past. We always talk about 'needing to know.'

Alfonso asked her if she knew why their family was in Brazil and Madeira. 'Your mother must have known as her grandfather would have told her.' Continuing, 'my father liked telling family stories.' Except he refrained from talking about events he found inexplicable because of unjustifiable reasons. 'Perhaps you were too young to understand. Perhaps, like me, she was too ashamed. Avoiding confronting the past, I remained in London,' said Alfonso. Our family were in the Order of Christ and the Society of Jesus in the colonies where they remained. They sailed between Africa and Salvador. Penny arrived, and they said goodbye to Olga Sara and Carlos, and Alfonso looked at the boy and smiled, 'You are our little brown warrior.'

By the time Joseph returned from Cuba, he became an advocate, having switched from smoking cigarettes to Havana cigars. With its combination of strong tobacco and a mixture of spices, it was advocated as being more effective at keeping mosquitoes at bay than cigarettes.

All the incomprehensible issues and challenges that Olga Sara and Emilia had been struggling with became distant memories. Joseph became unusually exuberant, waxing lyrical about the freedom of the Cuban people with access to better health and education system. Taking to recounting changes under Fidel Castro that had not occurred for decades under allegedly democratic governments and the dictatorship of Fulgencio Batista, Joseph now saw himself assisting Cuba's development through his work as its leaders appeared more amenable to change than he was experiencing in Brazil.

Important family matters, however, quickly replaced discussions about attributes of Cuba. Alfonso told his brother and Emilia that he and Caroline had separated and requested that they not divulge it to others in the family. He believed it was an unnecessary distraction. For example, he believed his elderly parents would conjure up reasons why they had not visited for eighteen months. Thinking that it is an opportunity for him to visit them, he suggested taking mother and child. Alfonso was surprised and disappointed that Lia Maria did not return to Portugal and Olga Sara had never visited. But it was clear why he identified with them as it reminded him of his announcement to his parents of his plans to marry Caroline Boucherett. The family, he believed, had a habit of not confronting reality or addressing personal issues. Predicting, 'if it did not change, it could be detrimental to the family's longevity.'

Part of his plan was for Penny to spend time with her cousins before returning to finishing school at Roedean, in Brighton, East Sussex. Founded in 1885 as a boarding school 'to prepare young ladies to enter English society,' euphemistically, 'a finishing school.' Caroline went to Roedean, and incidentally, Emilia was full of praise as she spent three months there when her father was based at the embassy in London. As for Alfonso, he and Dom Pedro agreed that he should remain in Sao Paulo and manage the financing of the infrastructure projects in the Amazon. Although disappointed with the change of Alfonso's personal circumstances and plans to visit Lisbon, Olga Sara warmly welcomed his decision to reside in Sao Paulo.

The 1960s, however, were not the best of times for Alfonso to live in South America. Political uncertainty and the armed forces reasserting their quest for power was dividing the country. Guerrilla movements vied to displace what they described as 'right-wing authoritarian governments,' purportedly replacing them with communists' regimes modelled on Cuba. A chorus of voices was advocating social justice and equality. Elements of the church and university were spreading the doctrine of Liberation Theology. The government, military and elites' response were that the doctrine was left-wing propaganda disguising communism. For the military it was anarchic, suiting its purpose when it wanted to disabuse opponents and impose order. Supporters of social justice were proselytising it as a force for modernisation and alleviation of poverty. Opponents, representing business and elites, however, advocated that the alleviation of poverty was best achieved by creating opportunities where each person's potential could be realised.

Casa das Flores was a house divided. Emilia and Alfonso, the latter although not attending church regularly, were advocates, while Dom Pedro held the conventional view of the business associations. Bea's opinion on all matters, except her infrastructure designs, was not to have an opinion, according to Emilia and undoubtedly Alfonso. Disruption in elite families, society and the Church led to rumblings in the armed forces, the latter is an institution that mirrors and reflects the community it serves.

COUP D'ETAT TO
MILITARY REGIMES

The history of armed forces seizing power and displacing civilian governments was established early in the colonial period in Brazil and in all Latin American countries. The period which impacted most significantly on the country and more generally, the region, had its genesis in the rise of the professionalisation of the armed forces in the 1930s. The military was never a professional institution as throughout their history they were subjected to the influence of wealthy landowners, businesses, and government, and a lesser extent the Church.

Experience in the Second World War and the subservient relationship to the United States contributed to the development of the Higher War College (*Escola Superior de Guerra*) resulting in a highly educated officer corps. The national security doctrine allegedly aligned the military with the principles of Western liberal democracies as a bulwark against communism.

The six-year revolution from 1953 to 1959 resulting in a communist government in Cuba, led by Fidel Castro, served to harden the resolve of the armed forces against communism. There was a steely determination to prevent the domino effect, which the US inculcated in Latin America, as many of the revolutionaries, most prominently, Ernesto 'Che' Guevara was from South America. The same doctrine was simultaneously propagated in Asia.

The 1960s marked a turning point in the role the military played in politics in South America. It was propelled by the United States taking a more active interest and even covertly participating in the politics of the continent, and more avidly and initially in Brazil. As the largest and most populous country on the continent, Brazil was of 'special interest' to the United States and had to be cultivated as the vanguard for the fight against communism.

Since the 1950s, US administrations wanted all the Latin American armed forces to be compliant with their policies. To achieve this objective, their defence department undertook a secret study of the region's armed forces. The Draper Report recommended that the State Department must identify the brightest trainee officers and either give them a scholarship to West Point or offer them training at other US military institutions. The plan was for these officers to effectively represent US policy and bring American values and culture to their country in the knowledge that any US administrations would support them when required. Under this policy, the military was encouraged to be proactive in politics. When the US was criticised for interfering in the region's domestic politics and supporting military regimes, President Harry Truman, famously said, 'They may be sons of bitches, but they are our sons of bitches.'

A program aimed at 'influencing' was not considered

a guarantee to keep Latin America free from pursuing the path of communism, which was already evident in Cuba in the 1950s. The country turned to communism in 1959. In 1962 the Cuban missile crisis nearly led to the Cold War becoming a 'hot war.' The US determination to keep Latin America under its influence resulted in the launch of *Operacao Condor* (Operation Condor) in 1968 which continues to reverberate in the contemporary era.

Developed by the US intelligence agencies and the chiefs of Latin America's intelligence organisations, Operation Condor was robustly anti-Communist and institutionalised violence against civilians. Most of the region's governments were either military regimes or was supported by the military. Under Operation Condor the armed forces were trained on how to 'professionally' kidnap and assassinate, and how to design and execute the 'disappearance' of any opponent of the regimes. Its most prominent and prolifically documented program was the overthrow of the left-leaning Allende government in Chile on 11th September 1973. And the waging of 'the dirty war' by the Argentine military from 1976 to 1983 against any opponent. Astonishingly, secrets of atrocities are still being uncovered in the present era, unearthing unfathomable excesses of Operation Condor. Unimaginable to contemplate that these atrocities were inspired by *El Condor Pasa,* a traditional Andean folk song.

Due to historical factors, these countries had a history of military regimes that lacked professionalism. In 1937

General Getulio Dorneles Vargas seized power. Propagating a policy of the industrialisation of Brazil that he expected would receive widespread support. The state of Sao Paulo's administration, however, opposed the policy and the state military forces staged a rebellion that was opposed by the rest of the country.

Vargas wanted to build the *Novo Estado* 'New State' and approved programs for the military to develop a modern armed force which would modernise Brazil. The size of the military doubled under his successor General Dutta. The corporate state was 'born,' and economic growth was to be inclusive. But the doctrine proclaimed that 'the state does not recognise individuals' rights against community rights.' In effect, 'individuals did not have rights, they had duties. Progress was to be above individual freedom.'

The result was allegedly nationalism and social reform. Ademar de Barros, a wealthy industrialist and significant landowner from Sao Paulo, oversaw a period of public works. An outstanding example was the establishment of Petrobas, the state oil company, with its monopoly on exploration which developed into a national institution that remained mired in corruption.

Business associations and families with historical relationships with the military positioned themselves to capitalise on opportunities. For the de Oliveira Evora, its established military connection and a record of successful infrastructure projects stood it in good stead. The Gentleman Club in Sao Paulo was complicit in the military plans and that is why Dom Pedro confidently proposed that his brother settles in Sao Paulo. Alfonso had visited many times but had no business connection. He trusted his older brother and advice from Portugal fortified his decision.

A period of turmoil eventuated under President Goulart. The elite landowners and business community called on the military to play a moderating role by taking power. Supported by the US administration, with its embassy monitoring the political situation as the communist and labour movement was playing 'a too active role in politics' Assistance to curb the movement was readily available. A cable stated, 'a contingent of the US military was on naval vessels offshore. Emboldened, the military seized power in 1964.

General Humberto Castelo Branco, a veteran of the Brazilian Armed Forces, received support from Minas Gerais and Rio de Janeiro garrisons. Crucially, it was not until the Sao Paulo regiment agreed to join with those two regiments that the coup plotters were guaranteed success. Brazil's and Latin America's history of the military seizing power had always been to represent the elite and industrialists and to protect the existing hierarchical institutional system.

The military regimes that governed from 1964 to 1984 created a perfect storm. There is a saying in Hebrew according to Olga Sara, 'those who sow the wind will reap the whirlwind.' Labour unrest resulted in regular strikes in all parts of the country. A liberation theology philosophy disrupted the Catholic Church and universities and ruffled the feathers of the military. During this tumultuous period, the Tupamaros guerrilla movement rose in Uruguay, fighting to unionise the sugar cane workers who had been mercilessly exploited in South America for centuries. The 1964 seizure of political power became the harbinger of military coups in South America.

Brazil entered another period of dictators in uniform. A popular misnomer of them as 'strongmen' is misplaced. They exert power through the barrel of a gun. Avowed anti-communist, law, and order were to be restored through a 'crack down' on all opponents. But most importantly, the regime's avowed purpose was supposed to be rapid economic growth with a focus on significant infrastructure development.

Governments, whether civilian or military, had been examining schemes to develop the vast Amazon basin. They advocated that its resources could be exploited to supply domestic markets to contribute to develop the country and alleviate poverty. Endemic poverty alleviation has never received serious attention from democratically elected or military governments. Civilian governments did not attain consensus as the political parties have historical roots based on self-interest. When the military believe that this becomes unmanageable, as with exploiting resources, then they are always ready to step in on the justification that they have the mandate to protect 'the national interest.'

Industrialisation was propagated as the overriding policy of military regimes. Economic recovery and growth were to be led and controlled by state governments and not federal. As the wealthiest and most industrialised state, Sao Paulo capitalised on its attributes. Contracts for projects were awarded to families, friends, and supporters of successive military regimes. For the military, 'loyalty was essential, competence was optional,' according to its critics. Military presidents were a mixture of ambitious and inept. Not educated in business and with no experience in managing a country's economy, they appointed cronies to manage these major projects. Once career officers' share of the allocated finance was assured and family members were engaged, work on the projects was guaranteed.

Dom Adenar de Barros, a member of a Sao Paulo landowning dynasty, was given the task of granting contracts despite being publicly acknowledged as 'corrupt and untrustworthy.' It was openly stated that 'he steals but he gets things done.' His links with the regimes were strong and his connections personal.

Mariam Leitao, an economic journalist wrote:

'family companies were assigned slices of the national market in the same way as in the sixteenth century. There is no modern capitalist in Brazil, only capitalist tied to the state who receive orders from the top.'

This was an apt description of the elite group of landowners and industrialists in Sao Paulo who controlled Brazil's infrastructure development.

While contracts were being awarded to favoured parties under the slogan, *Construa o Brasil* the military was otherwise occupied combatting anticommunism activities and a guerrilla movement. It resulted in constant unrest and kidnappings such as that of the US Ambassador, Charles Burke Elbrick, giving the regime additional reason to increase its activities in the Amazon to annihilate the guerrillas.

Waging war and economic development were conducted with equal enthusiasm. The project which the military regime used as a signature of its vision for Brazil was one of the largest, most expensive, and complex infrastructure projects in the world. Nothing of this magnitude had ever been attempted. It was the giant *Itaipu* hydroelectric dam which was built on the Parana river to supply power to propel Sao Paulo's industrialisation and Rio de Janeiro's modernisation.

The Amazon is larger than Europe. Brazilians are imbued from an early age that the *'Amazon belongs to us.'* Opening it up for development was widely acknowledged to result in the displacement of Amerindians and unprecedented environmental damage. Clearing and burning the forest made way for cattle ranches, mining, new hydropower plants, and many other projects. Brazilian governments, civilian and military, have been examining schemes to develop the vast Amazon basin, where they believed resources could be exploited to supply domestic markets to contribute to the development of the country, and to alleviate poverty.

A catch cry that has never been taken seriously given the establishment attitude to the poor.

As democratic governments never seem to reach consensus, the business community was always ready to instigate regimes to take risks. Some career officers believed that as they lacked experience, these projects could become unmanageable, using resource exploitation as an example. But others argued that the military must always be ready to step in on the justification that they have to protect the 'national interest' through development, equating it to serving the elites. Unregulated, domestic, and international agencies argued that deforestation would certainly prevail under the military, contributing to climate change.

Under the heavily canopied rainforest with its myriad of rivers, the Amazon is estimated to hold ten percent of the world's freshwater. The Parana River is the world's seventh-largest river. In 1973 the military government announced the development of the dam on that river on the border with Uruguay which was to be funded by the government and international financiers. The project was managed by British engineers. Dom Pedro declared that 'there was no one better suited to manage the financing of the project.' Alfonso de Oliveira Evora was indeed uniquely qualified and was welcomed by the British managers given his Portuguese ancestry but importantly his career in the City of London.

To build an infrastructure of this magnitude required a multifaceted set of skills. The most sensitive was 'the acquisition of land that would displace people and wildlife.' Environmentalists from all over the planet were complaining and questioning whether the damage caused was worth the benefits. Given its remoteness, protests were held in cities but were ignored by elites and carefully and closely 'managed' by the military and police. The military regime pointedly refused to respond to any 'misguided accusations,' according to media briefings. To combat 'misguided' opponents, the regime launched a public relations campaign to market 'the benefits to the country's development and to lifting people out of poverty.

Military officers were not skilled in public relations, managing the country's economy or major projects. This was evident by mismanagement and the significant cost overrun of the projects Many displaced people were not adequately compensated and although it was estimated that approximately one hundred and fifty people died, it was stated that actual figures can never be ascertained. By the time hydroelectric power flowed in 1984, the country was on the verge of returning to civilian government. Investigations into the mismanagement and financial burden of the hydroelectric dam drowned under the excitement of the regular supply of electricity to drive Sao Paulo's frenetic industrialisation.

Almost simultaneous with the hydroelectric dam was the regime's other signature extensive and expensive infrastructure project. The Trans-Amazon Highway was allegedly the brainchild of President General Medici, after a visit to the north during a period of drought in 1970, but more likely that of the business establishment. It was designed to cover 5000 kilometres *(3100 miles)* through the Amazon from northern Brazil to the border with Peru. Described as one of the most ambitious resettlement programs, it was to relocate poor people from the less developed North to the fertile Amazon.

Advocated and promoted by the regime as the most ambitious economic development program ever devised, it proudly proclaimed that civilian governments talked about this project but could never develop it. When announced land prices in the area skyrocketed as existing landowners, developers, loggers, and industrialists acquired and subdivided the vast area. From the sale, investors and the regime made a substantial profit. Yet the military touted its benefit to the country.

Projects were indeed developed which benefitted the country, but the major beneficiaries were a coterie of associates of the military and importantly senior career officers. The most scandalous aspect of the development of the Trans Amazon Highway was the unfettered violence and killings of protesters against environmental damage. They tried to bring to world attention the wanton destruction of the rainforest and the displacement and murder of Amerindians. Importantly, planning was haphazard, and the investigation of the soil and conditions were not examined. The result was a highway still unsealed and not in use for six months of the year in the rainy season when all forms of land transport got stuck in the mud.

A prominent and a significant beneficiary of the Trans Amazon Highway was the diversified conglomerate of which de Oliveira Evora was the principal contractor. A pregnant Olga Sara sought solace with Emilia and was inadvertently an observer on the sidelines. She saw much and said little. These women's testimonies were told to their journals. Malfeasance capitalised on incompetence creating opportunities.

Officers were regular visitors to Casa das Flores but visits and activities increased demonstrating a clear indication what the press was reporting. Night visits by officers out of uniform driving their personal cars as opposed to being driven in a military vehicle, was both witnessed. It was dangerous as students, unions, and guerrilla resistance staged uprisings against the division of spoils.

The military dealt with the protests, while the business community divided the spoils. To further capitalise on opportunities, de Oliveira Evora business diversified claiming it was to meet the economic development of Brazil. Because of their extensive network in the business community, the military, and the Catholic Church, Don Pedro apparently had the confidence of all parties. That was precisely why he anticipated the growth of the mining industry and formed a partnership with the military to build roads and other mining infrastructure. Roads were built to carry large and heavy equipment which was also the requirement for transporting material used to fight guerrillas and illegally relocate Amerindian tribes. Therefore, his business was a major beneficiary. The regime paid for the infrastructure and the mining companies also paid for roads. Paid by both, his companies distributed the proceeds.

While major infrastructure projects were being developed, nationalisation of some lucrative businesses mandated by the regime were sold. A successful pharmaceutical company, owned by the Jose dos Santos family, a member of the extended de Oliveira Evora and Setubal families was acquired by Pfizer pharmaceutical, a US multinational company. Other successful health industry companies were 'sold' to US entities, at a fraction of their value, from which career officers benefitted and owners received token payment.

The Brazilian economy was booming because of the Amazonian projects resulting in the transformation of *Foz do Iguacu,* the town close to the *Itaipu* dam. Allegedly, anticipating the change, the military allocated land, and infrastructure was built by the de Oliveira Evora to meet the growing demand for accommodation and offices. Among the mass of labourers, administrators, and engineers relocating to the town, were the occasional visit by international financiers monitoring the use of loans and simultaneously taking the opportunity to visit the world-renowned Iguazu Falls.

The 1970s was a period of frenetic activity marked by a significant change in Brazil, Sao Paulo, and in the de Oliveira Evora and Evora dos Barros families. Adelia and Estrelle were at college in Miami and New York. Olga Sara and Emilia wrote about the period as *avant-garde*, with unfettered music, poetry, literature, and gardening and imbuing Carmelita with the de Oliveira Evora family tradition, culture, and values. Strategically preparing her to be the purveyor of the dynasty.

Dom Pedro and Bea spent a significant period in Foz interrupted by visits to Sao Paulo. Joseph was in a similar situation, except that he was in another region of the Amazon. Promoted in the Ministry of Health to work directly with the WHO, his team was investigating the effects of DDT on the spread of malaria and elephantiasis. Alfonso on the other hand was still complaining to Emilia about his challenges on the project funding. He visited both locations and had a preference for working in Sao Paulo. Despite working in Foz, he had not visited Iguazu Falls.

Alfonso and Dom Pedro's relationship had undergone a renaissance. They overcame differences of opinion and matters regarding the allocation of funds. Alfonso had to compromise. He shared this with Emilia and told her that project sites were 'no place for a lady.' Clearly, he intended discussing it with Dom Pedro and propose that perhaps Bea should be spending more time in Sao Paulo where she can assist him. Uncharacteristically, on this matter, Emilia emitted a demeanour of distant independence.

In Foz Alfonso was so popular with the British engineers that they called him 'Al' and would often ask how he was 'adapting to working in Brazil.' Alfonso told Emilia, 'I had an inkling that they were referring to the presence of the military officers' frequent visits.' The richly resourced barracks were to be, 'a home away from home.' As a military stronghold, it was supposedly so that their presence would curtail the activities of the Tupamaros guerrillas.

Kidnappings persisted, facilitated by the fluidity of activity at the border with Uruguay. In the Amazon, borders were porous, generally not observed, or recognised by the Amerindians and acquiesced by insurgents. Dom Pedro resented questions from the British team and told Alfonso he did not approve of the familiarity, such as him being called Al, as it was not giving him the respect he deserved. Even asking that he curtailed the familiarity. It was a meaningless demand as Alfonso was well known for developing personal relationships. For Alfonso, their perception, which was soon to become reality, was Dom Pedro's conflict of interest.

These problems paled into insignificance when Gregory Bush, a British engineer declared that the dam wall structure needed fortifying. Work had to stop until the problem was rectified. Again, there was a cost blowout. The military government had to curtail a period of regular strikes and demonstrations against the Amazon projects, so did not want any delay in the construction to be made public. Dom Pedro had not returned to Sao Paulo for about a month and requested that Alfonso flew to Foz so that he can return to the city. A distance of approximately one thousand kilometres (800 miles) Alfonso was prepared to travel but did not see a need for him to stay for an extended period.

Before he departed for Foz, Alfonso serendipitously met Joseph at the Sao Paulo Gentleman Club. It was the first time in several months that they found themselves without the presence of another family member. One thing they had in common was their satirical elegance. Manners mattered as did the clarity of communication. Using the opportunity, according to Joseph's report to Olga Sara, Alfonso wanted 'to speak about a personal matter.' It was already five years since Carlos was in England, Alfonso thought he should raise this matter with Joseph, but it was summarily dismissed. A twelve-year-old boy in an English public school elicited little interest from Dr dos Barros.

Incidentally, Joseph was more interested in how Alfonso was coping with another delay and financial problems. It was later revealed that a memorandum was issued stating: 'The government had committed to pay for the project as they needed workers to stay on-site as the project will resume soon.' Apparently, the news was received with implacable hostility by Dom Pedro and the skein of career military officers. Yet the terms of agreement stated that before the funds were allocated, a forensic examination of the submissions was to be conducted before being sent to the Budget Office. Alfonso was to blame. What he and his team discovered were anomalies and unaccountable discrepancies which could not be verified. Reputational damage immediately occupied his thinking. Confronting a conundrum of this proportion was simply mind-boggling for him.

Alfonso told Joseph that Dom Pedro was returning to the city and declared his appreciation at the opportunity to meet, as Joseph was also looking forward to seeing him discuss his future, which he eagerly shared with Alfonso. 'Flushed with pride,' Alfonso told Emilia, he declared 'I accepted a position with the WHO in New York, which I will be discussing with my wife.' Emilia never broke his confidence. When Olga Sara informed her, Emilia feigned pleasurable surprise.

A boisterous discussion of the WHO opportunity ensued, perhaps facilitated by Madeira wine that opened the floodgate for conversation between Alfonso and Joseph. Flowing under control, the way the waters of the Parana were anticipated to when the Itaipu dam was delivering electricity to Sao Paulo. The popular belief was that it would guarantee that there were no further blackouts in the city. Alfonso avidly talked about 'getting a better appreciation of the idiosyncrasies of the people and work culture since he visited the site of the projects,' where there was hostility leading to an altercation.

He lambasted some officers and business leaders as 'charlatans.' Going as far as describing the cadre of officers in Foz as the last resort of scoundrels. Postulating that 'it all makes sense, but in fact, it makes no sense at all.' With a twinkle in his eye, Alfonso sheepishly described General Manuel O'Campo as 'a bear of a man with big hairy arms.' Vexatious, he demanded implacable vigilance from junior career officers as he was intoxicated with power and interestingly was a close confidant of Dom Pedro. Harshly describing his brother as a sycophant of the generals. These career officers did whatever it took to enrich themselves to join the ranks of the elite but were unobtrusively referred to as *nouveau riche*. Little said about the fact that they were part of the kleptocracy.

The General was always dressed in full starched uniform and his arrival was pronounced by his stomping gait as if he was still in the guards' parade at the *Bandeiras Palacio*, where Alfonso, parodying him said, 'he smells of brass and shoe polish.' Officers in this coterie were praetorian with direct access to the regime's administrators. An enigmatic inquisitor, his mere presence extracted information from enlisted soldiers. Responsible for issuing contracts, the General grandiloquently signed them, imposing himself as the arbitrator on any controversy. After all, he confected stories and declared that it is the absolute truth. Alfonso described him as a *'pasquinade,'* wanting to tell him it was his justification of the truth. Lampooning him with Emilia, they vowed not to share it with Dom Pedro.

Neither of them at that stage shared much of their 'confidences' with Dom Pedro anyway. Occasionally, it would frustrate him especially when he was in the Amazon for long periods with fleeting communication. Several times over many months when Alfonso lived at Casa das Floras, he and his brother would have altercations, seemingly without any cause or purpose but based on suspicions.

It was in fact, Emilia's relationship with her husband's

younger brother that became contentious, threatening to combust in an atmosphere where allegiances and secrecy were the accepted norm. Openly, Alfonso declared that the integrity of her character made her a beam of light in times of darkness in the mansion. Perhaps, the *joie de vivre* that was presumed to have prevailed was enough cause to sow seeds of doubt which threatened the pretend harmony of the mansion where cooks and maids were not whispering as they were unquestionably loyal to Emilia.

Listening and observing as he travelled the route where vehicles were often stuck in the mud, Joseph agreed with Alfonso that the proposed Pan Amazon Highway, was something of an experience, impassable during the raining season and a dust bowl in the dry. Alfonso criticised the lack of appropriate planning and costings.

The time had come for Alfonso to settle on his future, reflecting on his contribution to the family business now that he had been immersed in it as opposed to just raising funds in the City of London. Apparently, he shared with Emilia that when he returned from Penny's graduation in September, he and Dom Pedro will review his role. Alfonso believed he was not being allowed to fully contribute to the projects and was disillusioned, considering returning to England. Emilia would, after a major incident, reflect on that period detecting Alfonso's feeling of impermanence caught in an abyss of uncertainty.

Dom Pedro's perpetual mobility prevailed. Intoxicated with success, it was a habit he cultivated as a 'badge of honour.' Worn with pride he advocated it was his prerogative to build on the legacy of his ancestors. Families like the de Oliveira Evora instilled in their male members the merits of posterity which were deemed sacrosanct for providence: every generation bore a responsibility to thrive and to leave a legacy.

His delusion of grandeur was often talked about after the passing of Dom Fernando's soul, his mission was usurping his older brother's heredity rights. He prevailed by postulating being imbued with his father's spirit as his guiding light. Assuming the right to his father's position to determine the de Oliveira Evora destiny was fraught with unforeseen consequences. Obstinate in his purpose, he was to be permanently ensconced at Casa das Flores, a result of a concatenation of events, dispatching Alfonso to Foz in perpetuity.

According to Alfonso's collection of notes and letters, Dom Pedro could not confront reality. Well known, his intransigence was legendary and became his hallmark. Impervious, Alfonso did not curtail his perseverance. A scrupulous man of accounting after many years in the City of London, he was accustomed to forensically examining submissions for anomalies and discrepancies before presenting them to the Budget Office, to which his coterie reluctantly acquiesced.

Accustomed to speaking affirmatively about policies that were at variance with international financial institutions, General O'Campo was oblivious to the contractual agreements the government was obligated to adhere to under all circumstances. Prevailing in his determination, Alfonso wanted to discipline recalcitrance and uphold agreements while countering authoritarian orders. Realising, however, that the military had a tradition of vanquishing perceived foes. Challenging military authority was a subject of suspicion as they could mobilise and impose force on those opposing the regime's authority.

Alfonso was accused with venality for meddling, alluding to malfeasance by a cohesive coterie. In defence, he tried to show that increased capital inflow may amplify imperfections and would contribute to a financial crisis. With responsibility to identify and rectify shortcomings in accounting and the allocation and disbursement of funds, he was not prepared to accept the incomprehensible manipulated financial reports. As the situation deteriorated, his irritability grew into frustration. All of which culminated when he overheard his work described as, 'financial wizardry.'

Siphoning funds through a network of individuals and companies revealed a labyrinth more intricate than the Vatican Inquisition. Making auditing required by international financial institutions a feat of subjugating and cajoling irascible 'rascals.' They believed that it would expose the complicated financial arrangements constructed to camouflage the distribution of the spoils of the monopolies. An incensed Alfonso wanted to establish the parameters of governance for a coherent and cohesive strategy to build trust and accountability making it the anthesis of uncertainty.

What he never knew, but may have either assumed or believed, can be surmised from his correspondence. It was that Dom Pedro judiciously shielded himself behind layers of bureaucracy, always prepared to slither away. Alfonso wanted to observe the rules of international finance and develop a balanced risk portfolio for his brother. Both aiming to achieve the same objective: one observing the law, the other perfidious.

Embarrassingly confronted by falsified accounts the regime's fissiparous practices conducted by stealth were being exposed. Disillusioned, Alfonso planned his exit from despair as he was unwilling to succumb to aggravation from officers' mendacious behaviour and efforts to besmirch him by sabotaging his reports, which became intolerable, he wrote.

Retrospectively, Alfonso discerned that he was impelled to speak forthrightly, knowing that he could not provide cogent answers to the international financial institutions as authoritarian regimes masquerade as abiders of accountability but are purveyors of corruption. He foresaw the dangers and refused to submit to suppression. Crucially, if his recommendations were ever implemented, they would have been transformative for the regime. Defying their avowed intention, however, bode ill for Alfonso.

Allegedly, Dom Pedro's monopoly had a mysterious immunity to fiscal scrutiny. When challenged about the veracity of costs, explanations were rejected as confabulating numbers, amateurish and mediocre. Inevitably and forcefully dismissing the issues contributing to Alfonso's feeling that he was being manipulated, he demurred in stubbornness to reality. Pointing out that self-interest did not guarantee loyalty.

Career officers seemed determined to pillory him, besmirching his 'sanctimonious behaviour,' with an avowed determination to prove he was not sacrosanct. Bewildered at the antagonism, his lucidity and clarity of purpose were to achieve transparency, simplifying procedures to amalgamate systems to annul responsibility. Confronting reality, he may have thought, would appeal to their commitment to general prosperity beneficial to all Brazilians. For Alfonso, myopia was detrimental. Sacrificing his principles was unimaginable, irrevocably leading him to the precipice of unsuspecting calamity.

Considering that what he shrewdly thrived to achieve during his tenure was to curtail repercussions and for the de Oliveira Evora business not to be complicit in malfeasance. Crystallising his thinking he marshalled his forces to confront his older brother, and not to be succumbed by aggrandisement but preserving a family's questionable inheritance to his unquestioned values and professionalism.

Many years later Dom Pedro's prioritisation of prosperity would contribute to the loss of his family's legacy of dedication to empire building. On parting, Alfonso said, 'I am not a clairvoyant, but I have a premonition, *boa noite.*' Joseph left believing Dom Pedro was intoxicated with power making the situation irremediable.

Within three months of Alfonso and Joseph's encounter at the gentleman club, Joseph and his family moved to Forest Hills, New York, without an opportunity to say goodbye to him. The intention was for Alfonso to visit on returning to Sao Paulo from Foz. Olga Sara wanted him to deliver a package to a teenage boy. It contained a copy of the 1926 version of the Knights Templar, duty-bound to, as she ignited his interest later to turn into his obsession. Once in New York, Emilia told Olga Sara, they will have the pleasure of living in a suburb, unlike any other in the borough, where they can stroll through the Park and walk the narrow cobblestone lanes to observe the Victorian architecture. Enticing her 'to take tea' regularly at the English Tea House, in the village, 'located on the right just as you walk through the archway,' reminiscent of England. Perfectly described and with accurate directions from Emilia.

Meanwhile Penny was inconsolable when she finally found out that her father would not be present at her graduation. Nothing Caroline said or did mattered. Penny visualised her graduation photograph at Cambridge with her parents to pay homage to her Portuguese, French, and English heritage, and upbringing and indeed her parent's alma mater. Within a month of graduation, she was in Foz with her uncle Dom Pedro to visit the scene of the disaster.

Innocent to the tragedy, but for her benefit, the military

officer reiterated that Alfonso was sitting at the prow of the boat with a British engineer and two soldiers when it capsized. Allegedly, the diversion of the flow from the Parana river was swifter than anticipated. The bodies of the soldiers were found but not Alfonso and Graham. Requesting a thorough search and insisting on a more robust inquest, as both were British citizens, brought a verdict of misadventure, perhaps pacifying the British Embassy, but not the men's families.

Recapturing those memories after three decades, while knitting at home in Lewes, Penny was listening to 'Lark Ascending' by Ralph Vaughan Williams which was Alfonso's favourite piece of music. It was taken from a poem by George Meredith. Resurfacing with the rhythm was her animosity for Brazilian military officers. She told Olga Sara she had always wanted to tell General O'Campo, 'the only prick I tolerate is the one I get when I do cross-stitch knitting.' The perspicacity of her remarks demonstrated the astuteness of her judgement.

The long-awaited reunion of cousins where emotions were heightened from a week's pilgrimage honouring Alfonso and Emilia, finally fulfilling the promise Olga Sara had made to them by visiting the gardens in Kent and meandering on the hills and dales of the lake district. Dedicating that week to two people she loved dearly for guiding her during a turbulent period, Olga Sara drew sketches and composed poems which were preserved in her journal of May 1997.

Caught in the ambience of emotions, it was cathartic for the cousins as they expounded on their memories. Unbelievably confused, Penny could not give a reason for staying in Foz to work at the animal sanctuary caring for the wildlife that could not be relocated once the waters were released to flood the valley. Before moving to New York, Emilia, Olga Sara, and her children visited Penny. She wanted them to visit the scene where Alfonso 'disappeared' to pay their respects. The party took flowers and stood on the banks of the Parana river near the spot where the boat allegedly capsized.

Holding a bunch of flowers, Penny also tightly held a book of English poetry close to her heart. Standing on the riverbank she read.

> 'If I should die, think only this of me. That there is some corner of a foreign field that is forever England... And laughter learned of friends and gentleness. In hearts at peace under an English heaven.'

Embedded in Olga Sara's homage was, 'he had a trinity of attributes.'

Penny's lyrical cadence invoked tears that flowed uncontrollably as if in competition with the waterfalls they mournfully gazed at in the distance. Proffering that it was her father's favourite poem which she described to being admirably suitable in memoriam. Written during the First World War by a poet who enlisted and witnessed the carnage in the fields of Europe, knowing the toll was high and their bodies were being buried where they fell and suspected they would never be returned home even at the end of the war, Rupert Brook wrote the poem and died in France. Penny never thought she would have to recite the poem in Brazil.

A long way from Portugal and England, Penny's deep and abiding love for her father was unquenchable. She described him as the 'heart and soul of her family.' And 'for perfectly good reasons,' Emilia and Olga Sara knew they knew. Growing up he told her stories about his family's history during the Empire. Penny was indeed proud of both her parents' heritage.

Caroline and her parents taught Penny to take pride in her Huguenot ancestors who fled to England, escaping persecution by French Catholics. As a teenager at Roedean, Penny's pride in her father's heritage waned. This was a result of liberal education as opposed to her education at Catholic school. And indeed, time with her father when her parents separated, compounded by re-reading letters he wrote from Brazil questioning the Portuguese and Brazilian governments' policies over the centuries and the consequences. Those letters are now held tenderly and lovingly preserved as an important chapter in the de Oliveira Evora dynastic ambitions.

For example, the widely held view, which Alfonso propagated, was that he stayed in London to manage the financing of his family's business and because his wife did not want to relocate to Lisbon. Neither was true. Rather, at Coimbra and Cambridge Universities, Alfonso came to learn, then questioned how his family achieved its wealth and status, much to the chagrin of his grandfather, father, and brothers. But once he came to discover that most of their money was made from the slave trade, he wrote, 'They capitalised on it to make a fortune. I lost my faith in humanity.' For its hypocrisy and complicity, he rejected Catholicism.

Coincidentally, Alfonso transferred to Trinity College at Cambridge University, in the late 1920s where he met his wife. It was, therefore, easier to adhere to, considering his wife's ancestry and religion living in a Protestant country. He would not dare ask her to convert, as his family expected him to. It was clear that Alfonso was the errant son of Dom Fernando and Senhora Yolanda de Oliveira Evora.

At their farewell to Penny and Foz, after honouring Alfonso, Olga Sara asked her for details of the poem. In this highly emotionally charged atmosphere, she looked at the name of the poet; stumbled and fell to the ground clasped her hands together and prayed. Tearfully, she said, 'now I know why your father asked me and Joseph to name our son Rupert.' With Alfonso holding a special place for Olga Sara too, his request was honoured. Registering their son at John Adams School in Queens, New York she and Joseph followed an American convention. Their son Gilberto was from then, G. Rupert Evora dos Barros.

Intriguingly, on his deathbed, Rupert Brooke wrote to his two close friends making that request. A member of the Apostles, an exclusive group at Cambridge, Rupert received acclaim for being a war poet, when in fact he only wrote four poems about the war. Described by a reviewer as a 'mixed-up Adonis,' he reportedly died of septicemia from a mosquito bite at the Dardanelles during the Gallipoli campaign on St George's day 1915 on a French ship off Skyros, a Greek island, where he was buried. His death was described as 'one of the most famous deaths in English history.' Gallipoli will forever be remembered in Australia as the symbol of the country's identity.

From his voluminous correspondence published over half a century later, it was surmised that Brooke's demise was at his behest. Anecdotal evidence about Alfonso many years later led to speculation that the parallels between the deaths of these two Cambridge graduates may not have been merely coincidental.

Grieving in solitude for her father she sheathed home the responsibility to the Brazilian military. Penny demonstrated an obstinacy which was more akin to her uncle Don Pedro than her father. Rather than returning home or moving to an emptying Casa das Flores, from a house of constant activity, Penny decided to mourn in Foz. And in vindication joined forces to 'save the Amazon.' Environmental policy was not a feature of the two decades of military rule. Hopes were high with the return to democracy in 1984. In 1990 Fernando Alfonso Collor de Mello was the first president to be democratically elected and at forty, the youngest in the country's history. Pursuing progressive policies, President de Mellor appointed Jose Lutzemberger, an ecologist as Minister of Environment and a strong anti-military scientist, Jose Goldenberg, as Science Minister.

After two decades of what was arguably a blatant disregard for the Amazon dubbed by the world as 'environmental vandalism' the de Mellor administration was determined to make environmental policy one of its priorities. Penelope Boucherett de Oliveira Evora joined the team despite her uncle's protestations. Their mandate was to develop a strategy for the environment as the resources of the Amazon, so often touted as belonging to 'all Brazilians,' was being exploited for a few. Eager to make an impact and quickly, the team identified beneficiaries of the largess. Most were highly influential people but did not include de Oliveira Evora. Presumably, because the business was building infrastructure already approved by the military government and not developing agriculture which was responsible for vast areas cleared for cattle ranches and farming.

Midway through his four-year term, legislating progressive policies that were perceived as impeding elites' wealth creation, the president was accused of corruption and threatened with impeachment by the senate beholden to elites and wealthy landowners. This strategy continued into the contemporary era and was indeed a well-known feature and practice of the country's political system. Forced into resignation, most of his team also resigned. Expecting to be found guilty by a partisan senate but subsequently not guilty by the court of law, the de Mellor progressive team dispersed.

A fractious and divided country was again heading into demonstrations and violence. Dom Pedro took immediate action as the extended family believed Penny would be in peril. Her safety was indeed in question as foreigners were being kidnapped for ransom regularly. Defiantly protesting her Portuguese ancestry was to no avail as her father's reputation was under scrutiny, undoubtedly instigated by career military officers. Fear of her safety met feisty belligerence, but threats of deportation strengthened her uncle's obstinacy. *Tout de suite,* the *Senhora Inglesa* returned to England. A year later she was working with Greenpeace.

Civil action against the damage to the Amazon was violently resisted by loggers and land speculators who ran their own militias. The killing of Brazilian protestors went unheeded. It was not until an American nun, Sister Dorothy, was killed that the environmental movement, with United Nation's support, finally received attention from the government. Greenpeace and other international environmental organisations finally had an opportunity to work in the Amazon to develop a sustainable environmental policy.

Alfonso de Oliveira Evora was based in Sao Paulo managing the financing of projects. Dom Pedro and his office manager Bea were spending most of their time in the city of Uruara in the Amazon. Credited with having the longest road in the world as it linked the Trans

Amazon Highway with the hydro dam. Alfonso was joining a party of military personnel to spend two weeks in the Amazon basin.

His visit was scheduled and carefully planned for the first-hand experience of the projects and for conducting a review of expenditure. It also included an investigation to determine what the government can do to increase tourism to the Iguazu Falls, on the border with Argentina. Reputedly, the largest waterfall in the world, Alfonso was eager for the visit. He had seen Niagara. Emilia had seen both and told him Iguazu was indeed the largest in the world and offered a more spectacular vista.

Meanwhile, Joseph was spending most of his time in defiance of the military's plans to relocate Amerindians without their approval. And importantly, the military was overseeing and imposing a policy of continuing to administer the campaign of spraying DDT to eradicate the Anopheles mosquito, in which he was losing faith. His brief periods in Sao Paulo reverted to the experience of the previous three years when Olga Sara was considering the future of their marriage.

That all changed, however, when in 1962 Olga Sara announced what has been long-awaited. Five-year-old Carlos was looking forward to the new baby, while Joseph was delighted but ambivalent. The arrival of baby Carmelita received a mixed reception in the family. Emilia saw this as a welcome relief that would 'save the marriage' and Dom Pedro thought it would lead Joseph to take more responsibility. The chorus of voices included his brother Vincente who appealed to him to curb his indulgence in alcohol. Reports were that it was curtailed with the birth of Carmelita, and most certainly noticeable by all at the baby's baptismal fiesta.

It became obvious by her first birthday that little Carmelita was a spitting image of her mother, drawing unspoken but negative attention to Carlos from most of the de Oliveira Evora family, except Emilia and Alfonso. The visits from Joseph's parents were fleeting while his brother, despite his commitment to travelling to Lowestoft, Norfolk for Petrobras, was giving the children the attention and love his brother had inexplicably withheld. Unmarried and living in the city, Vincente always made himself available. Olga Sara was both joyful at the birth of her daughter and quietly despairing for her son. Alfonso, however, was giving him the attention he craved but was not receiving from the other men in the life.

At every opportunity, after the birth of Carmelita, Alfonso bought Carlos another book on the Order of Christ. Vincente had also bought into the act, so their 'little warrior' was becoming an aficionado of The Knights Templar and dreaming that he was but had to accept the Order of Christ. Increasingly Alfonso became a major influence on Carlos. On one of his regular visits, he presented the child with a large box containing a surprise. Telling the six-year-old that as a 'Knight' he needed to learn to play their game.

Summarily he was now to learn to play the game of chess which Carlos had observed Alfonso playing with Father Bridges, the English Jesuit, at the presbytery and was indeed curious enough to ask about the board game. A game of strategy played by two people, on a board of sixty-four squares, each with sixteen black and white pieces consisting of a King and a Queen, two knights, two bishops, and eight pawns. Alfonso's patience teaching Carlos was 'a thing of joy' for Olga Sara and perhaps frustrating at times to Alfonso and Farther Bridges, as Carlos's strategy was for knights to always stay on the board.

Never openly spoken but commented on, Olga Sara confided in her journal that as the children grew so did the noticeable differences between them: olive-skinned Carlos and white-skinned Carmelita. Boldly, their favourite Jesuit said to Alfonso, 'Carlos *pardo* Carmelita *blanca*.' Brazil had become a *mestico* (mongrel) nation, so the country defined itself through the categorisation of skin colour.

The Portuguese were indeed tolerant of mixed-race marriages. Unlike other empires, Portugal, a country with a small population, did not send families to the colonies, only single men. To increase the population, mixed marriage was encouraged by the monarchy and Jesuits. Initially, Portuguese men cohabitated with Amerindian women in Brazil but soon the Jesuits prohibited this practice and insisted that these couples must be married, and their children must be baptised so that they can be accepted into the Church. For centuries Brazil propagated a myth of racial equality. The reality was that the definition of race in Brazil was complex and ambiguous.

In places such as Salvador, where there were few Amerindians, Portuguese men cohabitated with African women. Offspring of these marriages were commonly known as *mulatto*. Some mixed-race marriages were acceptable, except in elite families where mulattos were not. Determined to minimise such unions, potential spouses were brought from Portugal or other parts of Europe, especially Italy. A short period after colonisation, a cornucopia of racial types proliferated the north as miscegenation became the norm for the lower classes. This led to considerable interest in the subject by European ethnographers. Miscegenation became an accepted branch of science. It contributed to the design of racial categories.

Scientific studies resulted in a consensus that there are seventeen types of skin colour in Brazil. Portuguese and other Europeans were at the top of the ranking and people of African descent were at the bottom. Resentment therefore ran deep as their indentured ancestors laboured to build a nation to which they had no entitlement. A country settled on the principles of Jesus's egalitarian message, evolved into a hierarchy of races. Education and opportunities were privileged by 'blood purity.' A legacy that hampers a country endowed with creative people and an abundance of natural resources from attaining the status of a developed country.

Alfonso, a keen observer of people, showed a great measure of objectivity on this issue and indeed in his correspondence, but said little. At Casa das Flores he and Emilia had ample time to discuss family affairs as Dom Pedro and Bea were away for long periods and both relished the companionship. They also regularly saw Olga Sara, Carmelita, and Carlos. Dom Pedro and Bea were in the Amazon basin otherwise occupied with the challenges of the Trans Amazon Highway. Joseph was also somewhere in the basin occupied with solutions to curb the incubation of Anopheles mosquito through other methods with the sole purpose of replacing DDT. Believing they were winning the war on DDT in Brazil, Joseph turned his attention to elephantiasis, as Anopheles is one of the three species of mosquitoes responsible for spreading the vector.

According to their journal entries, correspondence, and oral history, Emilia, Alfonso, and Olga Sara's get together was always an occasion to celebrate. The trio shared much in common from art and music to gardening. Alfonso introduced or reintroduced them, as the case may be, to his favourite writers such as D.H. Lawrence, E. M. Forster, and Virginia Wolf, the latter he held strong opinion about from his Cambridge days, which was not shared by Emilia. Wolf who lived at Charleston as a member of the Blooms-bury group, was indeed perceived not to be observing societal conventions. Olga Sara was not enough versed on Wolf to comment. She could, however, to his views on some of the composition of Francis Edward Bache. She reminisced on her mother telling her about his music, but not about

Ethel Smyth, the composer Alfonso waxed lyrically about in mellifluous tones.

Attaining a sense of established presence at Casa das Flores, Alfonso wanted to revert to his English proclivities. So, he took to requesting a full English breakfast, which he insisted must include Heinz baked beans. At least that is what he told Erminia when he taught her to prepare breakfast which she initially resisted. She was immensely proud of her kitchen which Emilia allowed her to take full responsibility for, to make decisions, and not to let anyone interfere with her culinary practice. Not anyone though, but a gentleman, unheard of by a cook in Latin America.

Erminia reminded him volubly, 'I am the cook not you, so you must not be in my kitchen.' She adamantly believed that men were not to be in the kitchen. A belief based on superstition she inherited from birth in Salvador where mothers invoked spirits to infuse love to cook the best food for husbands to guarantee a life of perpetual happiness. Alfonso took it all in his stride as he was accustomed to the eccentricities of the English, deciding to 'take breakfast at the Gentleman Club and dine there in the evening.'

Emilia asserted: 'you will do no such thing.' Respectfully, Alfonso told Emilia, 'I will therefore have to teach her to cook a traditional English breakfast and dinner of roast beef and Yorkshire pudding and for afters (dessert), his favourite was spotted dick. Delicately and with a hint of humour, it was best served 'swimming not drowning in custard.' Incrementally, Alfonso's wishes were realised. He gleefully converted the family to regular English breakfast and occasional dinners and would come to dub Erminia, 'Lizzie', a reference to Elizabeth David who single-handedly taught the English to cook. And many years later, Carlos learned from her how to boil an egg. Unsurprisingly, all these terminologies and many more entered the family and friends' lexicon making Alfonso the *palavra magico*,' loosely translated, a word conjurer. Stylishly dressed giggling maids assumed making up words was the prerogative of English gentlemen.

Exuding wealth and power, a purpose the mansion fulfilled in spades, it had succumbed to unrelenting commerciality, as Dom Pedro's determination was not to lose his grip on power and wealth which was now predominantly achieved by controlling and managing military infrastructure projects. Reflecting on domesticity and its negative impact, Alfonso recruited Emilia to bring credibility and panache to the home, which he knew it needed. Bowing to his erudition and eloquence, secrecy kept, they instituted a gourmet program. Skilfully implemented, despite Don Pedro questioning its utility, with Emilia's stewardship, an invitation to these thematically designed gourmet dinners of Russian czars and French emperors became legendary. Years in the making, and most extravagant, which captured column inches in the Sao Paulo society pages, was the costumes of Marie Antoinette at Versailles.

Initially, a reluctant host, as she had already engineered a monthly cultural soiree hosted at each members' home, Emilia was determined to keep the *Sao Paulo Clube de Cultura de Senhoras Exclusivas*, so as not to dilute its objective and indeed did not want to disclose the secret assignations. Incidentally, she hosted her soiree when Dom Pedro and Bea were in the Amazon. Emilia cultivated this Culture Club which delineated Sao Paulo's social stratification. Olga Sara was inducted into the club as a gift on her twenty-first birthday, as she wrote, 'great aunt Emilia told me they were, like me, educated and sophisticated.' Orchestrated like a virtuoso, purportedly sans gossip, it was to ensure Sao Paulo's establishment families maintained their culture in a rapidly changing society which was verging, since the 1960s, to a lack of respect for European tradition. For her, it was important as Buenos Aires was preserving its culture. Imagine it was not 'one-upmanship.'

Emilia's refinement, grace, and presence made her the perfect *Matrona.* Agreeing, as intuitively she believed Alfonso was indeed recreating a culture of which he regularly reminisced while adjusting to another and realising that the most appropriate approach was through cultivating personal relationships. Oblivious to the nuances, Dom Pedro capitalised on these occasions, mercilessly exploiting them with expectations promising lucrative opportunities from generals who became presidents and he, the sycophant willingly obliged.

In the mid-1980s with the restoration of democracy and fading memories of brutal repression, change was being initiated by the younger generation infiltrating society from the universities. The ladies of Emilia's soirees saw themselves as upholding societal standards. Younger establishment women were losing interest in formal evenings, wanting to embrace contemporary society and advocating *vive la difference.* To them, the privileged structured society ensured they maintained their privilege. According to her letters to Olga Sara during this period, the group was dwindling in size as most families were moving to Europe and the US a result of the gradual awareness of the excesses of military governments. She was contemplating returning to Buenos Aires.

Alfonso's interaction with the house staff, puzzled them and Olga Sara initially, as his behaviour was unlike Brazilian men. Dom Pedro would occasionally remind him that he needed to 'know your place; the servants know their place in my house.' An encounter much talked about by Emilia was when Alfonso angrily said, 'but they are not your property, as they were.'

Establishment families adopted the European model of referring to household staff as maids but with a prefix to the title denoting their function. Middle class and *nouveau riche* called their domestic staff servants. Emilia, having spent most of her formative years in Argentine embassies in Europe, created for her household staff what was sarcastically referred to as 'a uniformity of uniforms.'

Emilia structured a hierarchal system based on how she perceived her social community and demonstrating pride in her mansion. Emilia designed fashionable uniforms for the maids for formal occasions to enhance Casa das Flores' image. For Dom Pedro it was a perfect ruse to institute discipline and conformity.

The maids wore highly starched blue designer uniforms with white aprons and a small white cap. It was a copy of the *Kipa* worn by Jewish men which signified God was above, as *beresheet,* from the beginning. It was indeed a designer skull cap (*zucchetto*), worn by the Pope: the only member of the Vatican allowed to wear a white cap. Cardinals wore purple. Given her ambivalent relationship with religion, no one questioned why the maids wore a cap with such religious significance, and years later no one could. Chauffeurs' caps, however, were stock standard, as was their uniforms, matching those of other establishment families. In the de Oliveira Evora family in Sao Paulo, all the chauffeurs were former soldiers.

Outdoor workers formed a special category whether they were regular or seasonal. At Casa das Flores, Mendes held a status neither bound by duties or uniform, which seemed to be implicitly known by everyone, except those pesky usurpers whose fate was determined by the chauffeurs. Most claimed some 'special' relationship with Dom Pedro but without verification could never actually meet him. It is not surprising, therefore, that Mendes made no claim but was held in reverence by all. He wore the moniker of humility, being described as affable and well-mannered with the ability to be unobtrusive.

Households were matriarchal. Responsibility for engaging female maids was, however, the purview of men. Who interestingly were of mixed race and predominantly of Portuguese ancestry. Loyalty, trust, discretion, and respect were the determining factors for their employment. Upholding these principles, their future was guaranteed, and some were even considered members of the family, creating rivalry and gossip. Any indiscretion, however, resulted in dismissal and never to again be engaged by an elite family but rather, abandoned to a life of poverty, to struggle in the squalor and crime of a *favela,* presumably to be out of reach of their former male employer.

Dismissed servants, on the other hand, were likely to endure a period of purgatory, though no longer subscribed to by the Church. After a period of redemption, they were again generally engaged by middle-class families, as a class devoted to servicing families have always existed.

The outliers were nannies and governesses. Most were engaged in families who lived on plantations with city homes and travelled predominantly to Europe. They were indeed a special category of household staff as they developed an acquaintance of intimacy with establishment families. Some were known for causing scandals of monumental proportions resulting in bitterly divided families. Known for melodrama, many of these stories were exaggerated, supposedly depicting real life in Brazil. These *telenovelas* (soap operas) developed a following by the poor who 'dressed in their best' to watch programs from which they saw lives that were unattainable, but no one could stop them from aspiring to live.

The tension between the brothers became real, it intensified, and was exemplified by an altercation in the garden. Alfonso shared Emilia and Olga Sara's opinion of Mendes' 'green fingers' for creating an abstraction of colours with his knack of pruning rose bushes. It was therefore not surprising that Alfonso dubbed him 'Capability Brown.' Another reference and comparison, he made, with a popular English personality. On this occasion, as expected, it was a famous gardener.

Another, but a more memorable encounter between the brothers in the garden became legendary as it appeared to have been scripted. As chance would have it, working and sharing the mansion with Alfonso, it was inevitable that Dom Pedro would get exasperated. And when he did his emotions reached unsurmountable heights. Purportedly, it was based on a report that Alfonso was overheard saying, 'her embrace was tenderness of femininity,' resulting in speculation of intimacy. With a look of consternation, they pursued opposite paths. But who was the statement referring to? And who reported it to Dom Pedro? Not the maids for sure as they were all obsessively loyal to Emilia.

Uncompromising, Dom Pedro's pretext for the altercation was the new house rules and dining rituals Alfonso had surreptitiously introduced. With a droll expression,

Alfonso incurred the ire of Dom Pedro. Angrily saying 'are you trying to create little England here? Well, don't,' as he walked away fuming and treating Mendes as an annoyance. Alfonso calmly said, 'you can disagree without being disagreeable.' Imagine a man of erudition, deep in contemplation but being prone to frivolity, thinking, the summer sun must be getting to his brother. In keeping with his quirky sense of humour, he modified Noel Coward's ditty and sang, 'mad dogs and Portuguese men (Englishmen) go out in the midday sun.' jigging his way out of the garden. Now, imagine, Mendes, giggling while digging unobtrusively.

Alfonso was undoubtedly an Anglophile. His tonalities had a rhythmic cadence. He advocated good manners, especially table manners with the correct use of cutlery. He dressed in double-breasted English woollen winter suits and white summer suits. Many of the changes he introduced to the household were not always to the liking of Dom Pedro but welcomed by Emilia. Alfonso liked the garden at Casa das Flores, with its canopy of trees on the periphery and sun-dappled rose beds, strategically located on the undulating countryside, reminiscent of his home in Sussex.

When he sat in his favourite shaded area of the garden with Emilia and Olga Sara, he inevitably would encourage the latter to visit England but was known never to have discussed Portugal. Emilia endorsed his recommendation. Meant especially for Olga Sara's edification, he waxed lyrical about the undulating south downs of East Sussex. He and Caroline moved to Lewes when Penny was twelve so that she did not have to become a boarder at Roedean.

What he thought Emilia and Olga Sara would marvel at was the artistry created by the Bloomsbury Group at Charleston, a stone's throw from his home and coterminous to it. Enlivened, especially as he had made several visits, 'which one needs to do,' losing himself in time and emotion. What was not recorded or perhaps he did not mention was the ambivalent relationship between Bloomsbury and the Apostles, as Cambridge was their *alma mater.* Coincidentally, they had all, including Emilia's father as a diplomat, crossed path with Vita Sackville West who developed that famous garden at Sissinghurst. Emilia and Olga Sara were delighted to be immersed in Alfonso's erudition and remembered, and indeed spoke about his considerable contribution long after his departure.

Alfonso on occasion, openly declared how much he missed walking his Irish red setter, Ocean, on the South Downs, which he did every morning before work and when possible evenings before dinner. Dom Pedro was the first to suggest to Alfonso that he become a member of the Gentleman Club, one of the two in South America. The other was in Buenos Aires, which Alfonso was told had more of an English atmosphere, which he could confirm, as he, Caroline, and Penny had stayed there.

All the family knew the city well, as Emilia took the girls there several times a year for them to perfect their Spanish.

Alfonso quipped ironically at the enigmatic country, 'Argentina was settled by Spain and then by migrants from Italy. Now unlike other South Americans, although they live in South America, Argentines still think they are Europeans, but speak a concoction of Spanish and Italian. Not '*Buenos Dias*' but '*Bon Dia*.' Alfonso quipped ironically.

Emilia was growing to detect an atmosphere which was not conducive to what she expected 'in my home.' She told Olga Sara that she had to 'put things right.' Never, did she explain or apologise for Dom Pedro's behaviour. It was his responsibility, she declared. Surprisingly, Mendes was her priority so at her earliest opportunity she would be in the garden and explained that by calling him Capability Brown, Alfonso was giving him a great compliment. 'Mr. Brown,' she informed him 'was one of England's greatest gardeners. I know. I went to Hampton Court Palace which is one of the finest gardens in England.'

That, Olga Sara would recall, was Mendes proudest hour and 'put a spring in his step,' Recounting the encounter to Alfonso, without hesitation, he quoted Shakespeare, 'Shall I compare thee to a summer's day...' which among other incidents apparently contributed to making Dom Pedro suspicious of the relationship that was developing between his wife and his brother.

With Mendes 'sorted' the *Matrona* declared Alfonso her next mission. Having confided in her that Penny had not settled since returning home, for which Caroline held him responsible, she offered to 'share his burden.' He quickly reassured Emilia and told her he planned to be there in September for her graduation and will resolve the matter. Sharing with her instead, financing projects required him to regularly question General Cardoso about the allocation of funds without appropriate documentation and authority for which the general took umbrage.

Pointedly, the general declared he had the authority. Funds were being diverted for other purposes, sent to the United States and Europe which Alfonso believed was to pay for military officers' children's education and purchase of assets. Around the same time in the height of criticism of the 'Amazon projects,' there was much speculation in the press about the purchase of apartments in Paris and Madrid by military personnel. Questioning led to a rift between the brothers as Alfonso unwisely and regrettably, shouted to his brother, 'there is no honour among thieves.'

Maybe. What he later came to learn was that infamous Brazilian proverb: 'If you steal a little, you are a thief. But if you steal a lot you are the chief.' As a junior partner, Dom Pedro quite simply said that he expected Alfonso to 'simply follow instructions, rather than interrogating the officers.'

Others in the company, according to Dom Pedro, reported that his business practices were more akin to European standards than Brazil's, which Alfonso was told vociferously, compounding the ignominy, Dom Pedro condescendingly translated into English, 'you do not have an appropriate understanding and appreciation of Brazilian business culture, after working here for over a decade.' General O'Campo's advice was for Alfonso to spend more time in the field 'to give him a better understanding of why it was necessary to pay commission to officers who were regularly away from their families.' And as was commonly known, to pay for children they fathered out of wedlock and their mistresses. And not necessarily the same.

Astonishingly, despite his personal and work challenges, Alfonso took special interest in Carlos after observing the lack of interaction with family members and their network with the child. On the other hand, the cook, housemaids, and gardeners, all of mixed-race treated him like a 'little gentleman.' Jesuits, such as Father Bridges and Father Morrison told Alfonso, of having to punish some of the boys over their bullying of Carlos.

Perhaps, Alfonso identified with Carlos. As the youngest of three brothers, Alfonso was regularly reminded by events why he left Portugal. In the immediate post-war era, he witnessed the growth of migration from British colonies and saw the English attitude to migrants. Unbeknown to anyone, not even Olga Sara, who had taken him into her confidence, Alfonso explored options for Carlos's future. Politely described by Emilia as a 'maven' Alfonso was indeed a man who had accumulated knowledge, because of his global experiences and eclectic interest.

Finding a solution to what was surmised as 'an unspoken hindrance to be rid of this child' from a pillar of the Sao Paulo establishment family became his mission. To deny him the family's name was the next task. To accomplish this task, Alfonso solicited the assistance of the Jesuits, officials and friends in London, and a British engineer on the hydro project. Advocating and actively propagating for Carlos to attend a boarding school that offered a liberal education, Alfonso was a man on a mission. Within six months in a turbulent period in 1964, he achieved his objective. After discussions with the Jesuits at Carlos' school, Alfonso unburdened himself to Emilia. Quoting directly from her journal, it was 'the most difficult and emotionally convoluted encounter I've ever had with a man.'

What he had accomplished, Emilia found puzzling, but not surprising. She had come to know Alfonso much better since he moved into Casa das Flores. So, she understood and accepted his rationale. Recorded in her journal was Dom Pedro's alacrity in acquiescing. Relieved, he insisted on informing Joseph that a place was reserved in a public school in Surrey for Carlos.

Time was of the essence and Emilia took it upon herself to deal with the matter immediately, but with Olga Sara. That encounter must have been traumatic for them as neither elaborated in their journal. Astonishingly, within weeks Alfonso had an agreement from the Samuelson from Wimbledon agreeing 'to be the boy's temporary guardian.' Alfonso was a man of ineffable courtesy and respectability and earned the respect of his network and therefore they all willingly rallied to his cause as he had done for them, elicited from the eulogies at the memorial service.

What was never known, as he followed his family's tradition of the 'need-to-know principle,' was why and how Alfonso came to the decision. Light was shed on his choice of education by his older brother Dom Jose. Alfonso was an advocate of Portugal's President Antonio Salazar who was his economics professor at Coimbra University. Remembering the president declaring publicly, 'English public school is providing the best education a boy can have.' Additionally, Alfonso had the experience of the system from friends at Cambridge, 'who to a man, were boarders.' Some sent their children to Harrow, made famous by Sir Winston Churchill and Winchester Boys School, one of the oldest in England, where Caroline's brother went to school.

Emilia did express her feelings on this matter to Olga Sara who visited her when she was in hospital many years later. The conversation between them was ominous. Tearfully, Olga Sara told her of a recurring dream. Listening sympathetically, it was about a fleeting vision of a woman in a flowing white dress holding Carlos hand as they glided on a bed of roses in the Palheiro Gardens. 'I did not see her face, but Carlos walked reluctantly, turning his head longingly and kept looking back at me.'

Arriving in England in 1964, Carlos would repeat in his best English as best he could what Alfonso regularly taught him, 'how do you do?' and promised never to forget to speak clearly. A tall order, but one he strived to achieve.

SALVADOR THE SAVIOUR

Confiding in her journal, Olga Sara greeted the news about New York with a mixture of trepidation and curiosity. And in the margins, 'It will be New York daze or New York days,' in keeping with her habit of making annotation of significant events.

In Sao Paulo, she was surrounded by the only family she ever knew. Moving to a city as vibrant and diverse was something she never anticipated and was unsure if she wanted to. But it was not a matter of choice as circumstances were again to be the determinant. Sharing her travails with the only two people she took in her confidence contributed to an approach that would pay dividends she could not have imagined. Having spent time in the city, Emilia and Alfonso encouraged her to also embrace its parks and gardens, architecture, theatre, and museums and made special mention of the public library on Fifth Avenue, a combination of books and art. And convenient to the best shopping in the world.

Olga Sara's only request of Joseph was for them to visit Salvador prior to departing for New York. Unspoken but understood, she had not visited for almost two decades. For her, there was unfinished business and now that she would not be restricted by Dom Pedro, she could also conquer her fear by visiting places of her recurring dream and nightmares. Sao Francisco Church and convent were where she met Father de Souza who she had never heard about as Dom Pedro forbade any familiarity with men and even priests. What she longed to see once again was *Praca Padre Anchieta* square where you looked up to the steeple and cross and into the ceilings, arches, and walls lined with gold, silver, and other precious stones, decorated with carvings of birds and saints. Quintessentially a celebration of what the Portuguese Empire skilfully designed and African slaves toiled tirelessly to build.

A compelling desire to also satisfy her curiosity drove Olga Sara's other motivation to say goodbye to Mendes and meet his mother who he would mention at any opportunity. He perpetually carried her photograph in his back pocket. He had to leave Casa das Flores suddenly, according to Emilia, as his mother was ill and as she had no other family it was his duty to return home. 'Perhaps he may not want to meet you,' a surprising statement that came from Emilia as she knew how much Olga Sara appreciated his work in the garden at Casa das Flores and her home at Jardim dos Oliveira, which he created. Many times, he would tell Carlos how much he would miss him, but she hoped he would now extend his affection to Carmelita and Rupert. Olga Sara used to, given the opportunity, referred to him as having 'green fingers' and for being the aficionado of roses, 'which I hope he will continue to be, as we need him to tend the garden while we are in New York,' she explained.

Salvador had not changed significantly since she was last there in 1957, except that it was no longer as hectic a city as when it was Europe's major sugar supplier. Now its reputation, along with Santo's, was as a producer of agricultural products of which coffee was the largest crop. The city's baroque buildings and streetscapes, reminiscent of Lisbon, was what she wanted Carmelita and Rupert to see as it was like no other place she had seen and believed it would be for her children too.

Mornings and before midday were customarily visiting time before the sun reaches its zenith and Salvadorans were generally at *soneca (siesta).* Joseph and Olga Sara visited Mendes, leaving the children in the care of the maids at Casa das Evora in *Cidade Alta* (high city) located in a row of colonial *casaroes* (mansions) filled with ostentatious accoutrements. They were constructed from Portuguese marble and tiles and Brazilwood, on spacious grounds with splendid gardens, in wide tree-lined avenues of opulence, in stark contrast with the rest of Salvador. Commonly, these homes were a mixture of French art nouveau with balconies of English cast-iron railings encrusted with friezes. The interiors housed rooms of volume, with a spacious library where children spent many hours being imbued by governesses with all forms of arts and science. The culture they were being taught was European, surrounded by a city dominated by people of African heritage. *Cidade Alta* was positioned to look down on *Cidade Baixa* (lower city) and the first settlement for African slaves.

Pelourinho ironically referred to as Pelo was the epicentre of the lower city. Its full name was never used in Salvador as it refers to a pole with iron rings to which slaves were strapped to be flogged. When Joseph and Olga Sara arrived at the home in Pelo, Mendes was standing at the door, looking expectantly, wearing a welcoming smile. And appearing more confident than he ever did, or could, she believed, at Casa das Flores There stood a man, perhaps in his forties about six feet tall, muscular, wearing the signs of an outdoor worker, a mulatto with tight black curly hair, a sharp contrast to his light olive complexion and tweedy features.

Richly decorated in ceremonial accoutrement, was a city Olga Sara loved for its culture and spiritualism. Given her proclivity to orthodoxy, it was perhaps because of Salvador's fusion of Catholic rituals and African mysticism. Coffee, however, is the flavour of Salvador. Beans were ritualistically roasted, not too finely ground, poured over with water at the precipice of boiling, cooked for a few minutes, served sprinkled with just a hint of cinnamon. Defying other spices despite the fact that spices of every variety were unloaded at the docks close to her home. Pervading the salty sea air were scents of centuries that imbued the colourful houses festooned with an assortment of Portuguese and African trinkets and statutes of the Virgin Mary. That is what portrayed the culture of Salvador. Proudly from this city, Mendes's mother Olivia, was a *mulatta* from Olinda, Pernambuco, the state next to Bahia. Stating that her father managed a sugar plantation owned by 'the de Oliveira Evora people.'

An attractive woman of medium build wearing an interesting visage emerging from a younger and more attractive face, with dark curly hair in the throes of greying. Engaging, with a compelling smile, exquisitely dressed and perfumed, gentle in her style with eagerness to meet her son's 'Paulista' visitors. Pelo has been her home since Mendes was born and where she intended to remain. Sao Paulo was too big a city for her, but where Mendes would prefer her to move to, 'but there was no reason,' she said. Puzzlingly stating that Mendes may have to move instead of her. Looking sheepishly, he asked about Emilia, Carmelita, and Rupert and importantly expressed his concern about the gardens and indeed the roses. Olivia said, 'he always had a way with plants' and that was why he liked Casa das Flores.

Looking askance in his impatience observing signs of ill health, Joseph restlessly gazed at Olivia, eager to question her health. Reluctantly, but encouraged by her son, she gently pulled her long multicoloured skirt which matched the scarf now covering her hair, exposing only her swollen ankle. Joseph confidently diagnosed and confirmed Elephantiasis, when she complained about itching and being febrile all the time.

It is an infection caused by the Anopheles mosquito, which also spreads malaria, and a few other mosquito species, it was commonly seen as an affliction of women. Mosquitoes deposit eggs of the filarial worm in the bloodstream which produces swelling of the body extremities and untreated can affect the whole body. With Joseph's assistance and the diagnosis confirmed, treatment was successful which she reported in her correspondence with Olga Sara in New York.

Mendes, known for being taciturn, accentuated by the presence of the doctor, voluminously expressed his gratitude to Joseph and Olga Sara, proudly introducing his mother. And thanking the visitors for what they had done for his mother as he had been worrying about his homes and gardens in Sao Paulo. During the rest of the stay in Salvador, Olga Sara and Olivia spent time together as Olivia delighted in being with Carmelita and Rupert. It was on one of these evenings after dinner at the de Oliveira Evora mansion that Olivia offered an opinion stating, 'it has been many years since I have been in Dom Pedro's home.' 'It has changed much since I used to come here as a young woman.'

Stepping outside to enjoy the evening air, Olivia asked Olga Sara's opinion of Mendes. She praised his qualities and work. Olivia then asked what did Dom Pedro think of Mendes? A question Olga Sara admitted to herself she could not answer honestly but must answer to share maternal concerns. Holding her emotions at bay, praised him as they openly shared their love of their sons present and remembering her 'firstborn' in a foreign land.' Olivia said that as her only child, she tried to guide Mendes as best she could without the support of his father. Taking Olga Sara into her confidence, she told her that his father wanted him to be adopted or 'put into the orphanage at Pernambuco,' but her mother would not agree, so she brought up Mendes with the support of her family.

Confiding in her journal, Olga Sara wrote, 'It explained the ambivalent relationship between Dom Pedro and Mendes.' The sad fact is that she was not sure if Mendes ever knew. Olivia told him his father died in an accident in a sugar mill in Pernambuco, where he was making *rapadura* (molasses) a dark syrup derived from the refinement of sugar cane and used in cooking main courses and sweet dishes and for medicinal purposes. Olga Sara did confess to Olivia her curiosity in molasses and its unbelievable personal consequences. Olivia promised when Olga Sara and Joseph returned from New York, she would organise a fiesta where molasses would be used in both savoury and dessert dishes. The medicinal properties would not be prescriptive. Unanimously agreed, Olga Sara hinted at a Bahian dish made with Tapioca, from cassava flour, cheese, milk, and chilli served with molasses. By now it was well-known that the latter was not to be included in the dish. Going so far as to say that molasses was never a conversation piece in the family and her descendants.

NEW YORK DAZE

Dramatically scrawled across the first page of her new journal, but this time when she arrived there, were the words, she muttered on receiving the news and scrawled in the margins. 'Will it be New York daze or New York days.'

The city overwhelmed her and her children. She explained to them, as best she could, that they were visiting, just like when they went to Salvador and then returned home. From her journal and stories, she told, Olga Sara and Joseph were to be temporary residents for three years. Joseph was not helpful with their arrival in a new country and city, yet it was one he visited, and they had not, and they moved at his request.

Officials from the World Health Organisation were exemplars of courtesy and kindness which facilitated them settling with ease into that splendid Victorian house in Olive Grove, Forest Hills. The maids and assistants were bilingual. Recalling her childhood in Madeira, Olga Sara was not in favour of that arrangement. Her philosophy was that they must 'all adapt and adopt' to the country. She believed that it was conducive to making the children adjust better and avoid expectations of the privileges of Sao Paulo. She was undoubtedly drawing on personal experience believing that it was best for her and the children.

American English was, she wrote, to be the family's lingua franca. For Joseph she did not account on these matters. Presumably, because they did not discuss such matters.

New York in the mid-1970s was a cauldron of disorder. Adjusting to a city in the midst of economic collapse, rampant crime, and high unemployment presented unforeseen challenges as they had grown up sheltered in Sao Paulo. Scenes of decay were evident in most places. Forest Hills was an exception. Those most disadvantaged were predominantly African Americans. Ostracised and enduring prejudice, they were also most identifiably engaged in intergang violence and shootings with a high rate of fatality. Simultaneously, Sao Paulo was also witnessing strikes and street violence as the military brutally enforced their agenda by suppressing any form of resistance. But Brazil was enforcing a brutal dictatorship and the United States was a liberal democracy.

All United Nations agencies, including the WHO, instituted policies to ensure the safety of its employees and their families. For Joseph, New York portended a new lease on life. Now an exemplary husband, in private life his family was a priority and in public, his commitment was to the organisation. At social functions, alcohol was imbued to proudly advocate Madeira wines. Perhaps the harbinger was the frequency of being pushed away by tiny hands as he tried to kiss his children with their 'you smell' and turned up noses. But allegedly a contributor was the recognition he believed he deserved and received for his contribution to the amelioration of malaria in Latin America.

In their frequent correspondence, Olga Sara freely admitted that she was now more engaged and supported Joseph's life and work. She more clearly understood what was driving him in his quest to see the eradication of the Anopheles mosquito and his determination to expose the dangers of DDT. Acknowledging her interest, Joseph told his wife about witnessing Amerindians dying from malaria, knowing that antibiotics were not a solution. And having to administer out of date drugs, bought at a discounted rate from US and European multinational pharmaceutical companies. Accurate in his observations, which OXFAM reported in Bitter Pills, and with the other agencies exposed 'Big Pharma's,' fraudulent practices. Vindicated, he vociferously, declared his frustration and feelings of helplessness.

At official functions and casual gatherings, a wife saw the respect accorded her husband for his 'field experience.' Acknowledgement from his peers led to the design of solutions as most WHO bureaucrats had little or no exposure to the areas of infestation. With the robust campaign, the WHO and some governments in South America, Africa, and Asia pursued, did contribute to the decline in malaria in the 1990s. Resistance, however, developed to antibiotics and new programs were being developed with personal philanthropy.

Olga Sara also believed that Joseph carried a 'burden of responsibility,' believing much was expected of him.

Although he was not representing Brazil, as he was working for the WHO. Nevertheless, he still felt a burden of responsibility and did not want to disappoint the country. Joseph rose to prominence in a country where ancestry and family networks were the overriding factor for advancement. Yet he achieved his position on merit.

With Joseph at work and Carmelita and Rupert at school and knowing they were safe under the security provided by the UN, Olga Sara decided to 'make time for herself,' as she wrote in her journal. She took summer courses in philosophy at New York University in Washington Square, imbued in the atmosphere both at classes and in robust discussions in the hallowed halls of academia.

Student demonstrations she witnessed at the Square in Greenwich Village, had little comparison with Sao Paulo, where the military was always in readiness to provoke and violently quell students' protests. Perhaps the square had a sense of reverence as it was built to commemorate the centennial inauguration of George Washington as President of the United States. Well known for its marble arch entrance, modelled on the Arc de Triomphe, it was the scene of many students' demonstrations she witnessed which left an indelible impression on her, especially for its educational value such as about the Holocaust.

Olga Sara not only wrote in her journal, but recounted the impact lectures by Noam Chomsky, linguist, and philosopher, had on her. Most remarkably, she wrote, 'he ignited my passion for ideas.' Actively engaged with students, he addressed demonstrations on the US's role in Latin America. Chomsky was admired as he was articulate in advocating current causes in his wide-ranging address on global issues. Reinvigorated, these opportunities reawakened her suppressed interest, questioning issues she was advocating and indeed solutions applicable to both US democracy and Latin American dictatorships. In the1970s most of the region was under military rule. Olga Sara became an advocate of Chomsky and encouraged by him, enrolled in religious studies, a subject, brought up as a strict Roman Catholic, she was never able to discuss in Brazil.

A confluence of circumstances propelled her to surreptitiously immerse herself in the study of Judaism assuaging her ambivalence. Regular discussion with a rabbi, encouraged by Joseph and Carlos's enlightenment to his mother's ancestry, informed his curiosity through friendship with Tony Levi. The family lived in Golders Green, north-west London, and invited him to participate in the observance of Jewish holidays which mother and son avidly discussed, uncovering the paucity of her religious education. Acquiescing, Olga Sara divulged her astonishment that the nuns did not teach the girls at St Francis the genesis of Catholicism. Feeling quite embarrassed when her ignorance was exposed in a debate about Jesus' intentions in his preaching.

To discover he was Jewish, and his teachings are the foundation of Catholicism, 'blew my mind,' she wrote. The thought that occurred to her was that at fourteen the nuns suggested she join the Order of St Francis. That, she reflected, would have been a 'fundamental mistake' quite unlike the mistake she made at seventeen. Both, she stated, were lifetime commitments. With time and with her immersion in the Torah and teachings of Jesus, she came to question whether he inadvertently started another religion when he intended to reform Judaism. Christianity was regarded as a sect of Judaism. Followers were referred to as Jewish Christians. During periods of persecution of Jews by Christians, the great Muslim leader Sulieman protected Jews in Jerusalem and accused Christians of denying their Jewish heritage.

This was a conundrum Olga Sara knew could never be resolved. But with the Second Vatican Council of 1962 which examined the relationship with the modern world and most importantly it's turbulent past with Judaism, there was no longer the need to lurk in the shadows. Laxity and the abundance of resources on the subject, to peer into the past, Olga Sara's singularity of purpose was to find some evidence of her father, if not him.

Assistance with her quest was feverously supported. A city with a sizeable and intellectually active Jewish population, where her mother told her that her father had planned to live, presented multiple opportunities. Enthused with heightened confidence, she had to temper her quest as it was approaching the fiftieth anniversary of the end of the second world war and most of the interest was on the elderly survivors of the Holocaust. Most had not or had reluctantly offered snippets of the atrocities and inhumanity they either experienced or witnessed. Olga Sara was on a steep learning curve. While relishing what she was learning, she was bitterly disappointed with the lack of knowledge about the schizophrenic approach which determined the treatment of Jewish refugees under the Portuguese and Spanish governments, and of more relevance was Portugal's dictator Salazar's attitude to Jews entering Madeira.

Immersed in Lia Maria's journal and family photographs, and Tascha's sketches and architectural drawings, Olga Sara suffered a crisis of nightmarish proportions from her dreams. Regularly waking up, struggling to breathe, choking from water flowing into her mouth, imagining her father's watery grave in the Atlantic. Rather than deterring her, she believed that if her father had arrived in New York, she would certainly find out through her willingly helpful network of academics, rabbis, and Simon Wiesenthal Centre in the city. And she did.

Learning that Tascha Rostowsky did reside briefly in New York, working for several architectural firms energised her quest. Garnering resources, with a determination of righting a wrong for a father not given an opportunity to know a daughter, she traced his journey from Funchal to Rio de Janeiro from the ship's manifest. Although the details of his 1940 journey were not clear or precise, her father had certainly not disembarked in Funchal as Jews were barred from 'stepping foot on the island,' on the strict orders of Salazar.

Staying on the ship carrying a cargo of cork to Havana, was where he had to disembark. Living there for over a decade, he was able to depart for Miami before Fidel Castro's revolution. Years of searching divulged what she had suspected. Tascha lived in Miami and New York where he achieved his dream of becoming an architect working on several significant developments from the late 1960s but returned to settle in Palm Beach. For his daughter it was a most unsatisfactory conclusion, as there are no known Rostowsky's from this Ukrainian family anywhere in the world. Unaccompanied to mourn in the solitude of her silent pilgrimage to his grave, the orphan knelt in prayer in homage to a father she never knew, except from photographs and sketches.

Awakening to the complexities that were unravelling, and from what she was experiencing and witnessing in New York, Olga Sara was determined to seek solutions. Conversations and frequent correspondence with Emilia were influencing her to seek her true cause. Opting to be an advocate for social justice in Brazil, as the military regime was mired in corruption and accusations of human rights violations, was fraught with disaster. Thinking the United States offered protection from Latin American regimes, opponents had a rude awakening when in September 1979 Orlando Letelier, and his colleagues were killed by a car bomb in Washington DC. Chilean dictator, General Augusto Pinochet was linked to the murder. Latin American regimes' opponents soon sought asylum in Scandinavian countries.

Speculating in her journal, as she was afraid to write about this subject to Emilia, Olga Sara believed her to be apoplectic with the public display of military power and suppression. Growing frustration with her situation and with Dom Pedro and social isolation for fear of the opprobrium took its toll. Joseph politely listened to Olga Sara's impending plans for when they returned to Sao Paulo but advised her not to engage his colleagues' wives or attract attention as it would impact on him at an organisation 'that must focus on science.'

Seeking divine intervention through soul searching, Olga Sara and her children regularly attended church. Joseph attended on the obligatory occasion of Christmas, Easter, and family members' religious observance. The choir, which Olga Sara had not taken 'seriously' since she sang at Funchal Cathedral, was realised in participating at St Joseph's in Queens. Sermons were of a different tenure to those in St Francis in Sao Paulo. Less strident, American Jesuits did not want to openly be advocates of liberation theology, given the US administration's, and the historical injustices of McCarthy's anti-communist witch hunts and ardent support of Latin American regimes.

In conjunction with the Church and as a member of the 'WHO Wives Group,' Olga Sara helped to feed the poor and hungry, and they all 'leant an ear' to the grievances African American mothers were voicing about their children. 'Sons and Guns,' as violence continued to suffuse a divided America. These women quietly persisted believing they were making a difference. Disillusionment pervaded the group when a church official told them they were 'whistling Dixie.' An expression they had never heard. It warranted a detailed entry in her journal on 17 December 1979.

Reflecting on her experience in Bahia and Salvador, with the largest population of Brazilian Africans, Olga Sara saw a common theme of disadvantaged and disenfranchised people, who because of a lack of opportunity, expressed the belief that the governments of these countries were obligated to compensate them for what their ancestors suffered. They held a strong belief that without 'their labour which built these countries,' Brazil and the United States, as examples, would not have achieved economic development. Empathic, Olga Sara, believed there was a case for *noblesse oblige,* identical in both countries, but neither honoured it. As a first-hand witness of the discrimination suffered by descendants of African slaves, her attitude was gradually changing.

Almost simultaneously, Olga Sara's attitude towards the military in Brazil was changing too. She received, from an unidentified source surmised to be at the UN, an early copy of *Brasil: Nunca Mais.* Edited, by Cardinal Paulo Evaristo Arns, the Metropolitan Archbishop of Sao Paulo. It was testimony to the military regimes' 'acts of unimaginable cruelty.' It was a meticulous record of torture conducted from 1964 to 1979. Obtained by a Presbyterian minister, Jaime Wright, it was credited with contributing to Brazil returning to democracy in 1984, with the election of a civilian government in 1985.

The Cardinal wrote: 'We observe the Gospel precept that counsels us to know the truth.' Details of the truth of torture were chilling. When priests and nuns were tortured, the Church, initially a supporter of the coup, was vociferous in its condemnation. On seizing the government, the military abolished all rights of politicians for a decade. It specifically targeted university students and abolished their union, as they were accused of being agitators under the previous government of President Goulart. The military's actions against those who were assisting workers in the Northeast, in places such as Salvador was recorded by commentators 'as senseless violence.' Carefully documented municipal and church records highlighted the fact that poor farmers and alleged communists were the largest group to be subjected to all forms of torture and 'disappearance.'

The military coup d'etat of March 1964 was under the pretext of suppressing communism and returning the country to democracy. Olga Sara well remembered that tumultuous year. It was a culmination of the uncertainty which started in the early 1960s when wealthy landowners and industrialists in Sao Paulo were agitating for a change of government.

President Goulart was pursuing land reform so that people in rural areas could own land and determine their future rather than relying on landowners. The next step, according to the president, was urban reform which was the 'straw that broke the camel's back,' as it was a direct threat to the wealthy families of Sao Paulo where most of the country's wealth is concentrated. On the 19 March 1964, Catholic women were demonstrating against the president and in support of the military. It had an estimated attendance 500,000.

Casa das Flores was a hive of activity supporting the military. Dubbed at times, *Casa para todos*, regular visitors were from the church, military, and business. Visitors, apart from the clergy, meaning military officers, never wore a uniform at the house. Increasingly, in early 1964, many boisterous, late-night parties, Emilia told Olga Sara, caused significant disruption in her relationship with Dom Pedro.

Finding a solution, Dom Pedro and Bea hosted the functions, while Emilia reverted to spending time in Buenos Aires, which incidentally was also mired in violence. But her father's military-diplomatic status was her reluctant shelter. Reflecting on what she had learned from Joseph, the press, and witnessing in the streets, families they all knew supported a military takeover of government. So much so that families sent their children to school and university in the US or Europe. Adelia and Estrelle were safely tucked away in college in Miami.

The business community was avid supporters of the military as it promised economic development, from which those associated with the military most benefitted. Initially, church sermons did not criticise the military, but in the early 1970s as Joseph and Olga Sara was preparing to leave, liberation theology became more pervasive and criticism of the government and calls for a return of democracy were overwhelming.

Grappling with these issues from the late 1970s in New York, Olga Sara tried to find answers for herself, to the injustices she was seeing in the media, specifically in Latin America and indeed the United States. Something Olga Sara would not share publicly was her 'total abhorrence' of the armed forces. What she saw in the media made her recall the arrogance displayed by career officers visiting Casa das Flores, and how soldiers treated people they stopped on the streets. She thought it was a direct result of officers cocooned in barracks where they only interacted with other officers and never enlisted soldiers or the public.

Growing up in a turbulent period, she was keen to educate her children on the vagaries of the society they lived in while trying to shelter them from the country where they were born. But it became complicated. Joseph asked her to let them determine for themselves rather than influencing their decisions. New York quickly became 'home' for Carmelita and Rupert. Struggling with contradictions, Olga Sara realised that she was going against her philosophy of 'adapting to the society in which you live.' But it was not the time to rally against social inequality.

Activism in New York was interrupted by preparation for returning to Sao Paulo in 1976. Instead, WHO sent Joseph to the Geneva office on a six-month posting. His field experience and unflinching commitment to finding a cure for malaria and a substitute to DDT became his hallmark and gained admiration from those who knew his story. Accepting plaudits, however, did not come easy to him. In Geneva, he quickly assumed his work ethic, which meant Olga Sara, Carmelita and Rupert had to learn to cope with the disruption. The children went to the international school and Olga Sara immersed herself in socialising with her husband's colleagues' wives as they were all in a similar situation in a city of global institutions.

'The elephant in the room,' however, was Carlos. Tucked away in Surrey, communications between him and the Paulistas had always been intermittent. An occasional letter from his mother was not about the family, but about his 'life in England.' Both were avoiding life matters. Substantive information about the family came from Joseph's brother Vincente who worked for Brazil's oil company Petrobras which was perpetually mired in corruption. Carlos shared with Vincente that he has been accepted to medical school. To his chagrin, however, arrangements were made for him to spend Christmas of 1974 in Geneva.

With an absence of contact for ten years, punctuated by irregular correspondence, and an occasional visit from a member of the family, an unexpected invitation was a total surprise. For one simple reason: he had never been kept informed about the family and had never met Rupert. Plans of riding and participating in his first fox hunt at his girlfriend's family farm in Sussex had to be cancelled.

Disappointment embroiled him with uncertainty. He may never again get to spend time with the rider wearing the red coat or to blow the horn for the master of the hounds, as he had always been eager to show Caroline his flamboyant musical virtuosity. Something he did not believe he had achieved as a member of a 'boy band' at school.

Reluctantly arriving in Geneva, emotionally perturbed on being greeted by his mother as if for the first time. Then told they were going to Marin, a suburb of Neuchatel. Festooned with decorations and lights, a wintry Geneva Christmas was in the air.

An emotionally charged reunion escalated upon meeting his sister Carmelita who he last saw as a two-year-old. Rupert was distant as they had never met and were strangers. What was unexpected was how easily mother and son bonded, 'as if we had never parted' she would with great flourish scrawl in her European journal. Neither was to know that what was occurring amidst the crisp air and beauty of *Marin-Epagnier* a municipality of Neuchatel in the Swiss Alps was 'historic.' To imbue and appreciate its beauty they adopted the local tradition of 'taking a promenade' along the lake; occasionally joined by Carmelita and Rupert 'to take in the air.' At seventeen, and over three weeks, punctuated with regular promenades, Olga Sara divulged Carlos's ancestry and the de Oliveira Evora's historical conspiracy of silence.

The story, up until 1974, was known to only a few in the family. It was a revelation that he reconciled with decades later for the simple fact that he had told a different story as he did not know his real identity. Like mother, like son, Olga Sara was known to say about them. Carlos was disappointed and remained dismayed that he never bonded with Joseph and his son Rupert. For Olga Sara and Carmelita, it strengthened over the years despite the infrequency of contact.

Returning to Surrey, Carlos better understood why people speculated suspiciously about his visage and origins. For him, everything would now be different. Or so he thought. Returning to New York, his mother wrote to him, Joseph was optimistic, confident with the research he was engaged within Europe. What impressed him most, as he settled into medical school, was Joseph having an opportunity to pursue research at Max Plank Institute in Germany. It was where scientists were experimenting with environmentally friendly substances for the treatment of malaria. Discovering that for his contribution in Geneva, the family would remain in New York for the foreseeable future.

Olga Sara's correspondence and communication with Emilia continued to be prolific, sharing with her places she recommended they visit while living in Europe. Emilia was eager to draw attention to Estrelle and Adelia's decision not to return to Brazil which Dom Pedro supported. In the late 1970s, unrest in the streets of Sao Paulo was a regular occurrence. Emilia accepted their reasoning and their father's acquiescence but suggested they return when democracy was restored, which was commonly accepted to be by 1980.

What most alarmed her was the lack of any contact between Olga Sara and 'the girls.' It did not surprise her, as much as it did Emilia. Olga Sara's friend Rose, who also lived in Miami told her that Estrelle was busy with religious studies. Purportedly, she was converting to Judaism to marry Stanley Hoffman, much to Rose's disdain. He was studying to be ordained a rabbi. Olga Sara did not offer an opinion but vowed to keep it a secret.

By 1980, New York started to experience the 'green shoots' of economic recovery with slow growth and a crackdown on gang violence which led to its abatement and less criminality. Democracy was not restored to Brazil as expected, and most of Latin America remained under military rule. But Brazil was incrementally in the throes of restoring a semblance of order as the military's extensive and expensive infrastructure programs provided employment contributing to an easing in strikes and general disorder.

A general weariness was overcoming many in the business community as both the Itaipu Dam and the Pan Amazon Highway were not achieving their milestones and accusations of corruption were rife. This led the military to hold to account officers responsible for the projects resulting in some being transferred to Brasilia and Rio. Dismissed and demoted officers and officials, in turn, accused the businessmen of mismanagement. The rift that developed between the military and the elites was compounded by what had already been publicly displayed between the church, the military, and the business community.

During this period of turmoil, Emilia suddenly passed away. Olga Sara returned to the flickering lights of a city and a family disintegrating in inertia. Bea was stoic while Dom Pedro, Adelia, and Estrelle were hysterical with grief in the superficial resplendence of a mansion that had lost its soul. Olga Sara was inconsolable. Casa das Flores was not the home she remembered, with an embarrassment of riches. Now, a mere shadow of itself. The spirit of the house of resplendently dressed uniformed maids no longer danced. Their music had stopped. Stories that emanated were reinterpreted and became legendary. Everyone, even those who were not present or were not born, told their version. Olga Sara, try as hard as she could, could not, rectify inaccuracies. It was a salutary lesson on how the de Oliveira Evora atavistically preserves their dynastic ambitions.

Dom Pedro's need for opulence had persisted and was all-pervasive, in stark contrast to what was happening in most of Sao Paulo and the rest of the country. Continuing to live a life as if nothing had impeded on his family's lifestyle. Mendes left to return to Salvador and the new gardener certainly was not any sort of 'Capability Brown.' Olga Sara wanted to visit Salvador, but Dom Pedro forbade her, and no one contradicted him to support her. Olga Sara decided she 'hated' Brazil and the people and kept telling Joseph she must return while he tried unsuccessfully to console her. With little recent visits, he could not offer any constructive suggestions.

Solemnity pervaded the dinner before her return to New York and her cousins return to Florida. It portended a display of the change that was approaching. Marked by a quiescence, unusual for a family who generally spoke in several languages in the same sentence over each other and finished each other's sentences, when someone was considered too cerebral or simply tardy. Hardly anyone spoke. Not even the parade of maids. Serving each course, they swiftly took leave. Prescient. This was unlike any dinner at Casa das Flores. Olga Sara wrote, 'the candles were not burning, but no one had the authority to light them.' Observing the evening's convention was beyond Adelia's level of endurance. Looking at the cluttered table as it was painstakingly cleared ready for coffee, Dom Pedro's impatience was palpable, so he aimed for a quick 'getaway.' Taking his leave, she interrupted his departure, 'I must say something,' stopping him in his tracks. She disclosed Estrelle's plans to marry a Jewish gentleman providing details of the relationship since university and details of his family in New York. Startling Estrelle who had sat in silence throughout the dinner, waiting for an opportunity to talk about her impending marriage. Dom Pedro cogently demanded an explanation. With acknowledgement and tears, her sister was there for support in her hour of need. At that moment Bea quietly slipped away.

Standing, Dom Pedro must have deliberately stretched to his full height of six foot two inches, to tower over proprietorially, with arms flailing frenetically. Angrily gesticulating in his abundance of fury, blurted out words, which they all heard and swore to each other must never be repeated in a good Catholic family. Convincing themselves that it must have only been uttered by military men in barracks but not on Remembrance Days. Tensions of decades simmering in a cauldron exploded like a volcano. Turning to Olga Sara, who sat quietly thinking that she was only an observer, he accused her mother of the cause of this situation as she had with the death of her grandparents who both died of pneumonia.

Bursting into tears from those accusations, Olga Sara was compelled to defend her mother, but decided against it and chose to leave the room, when he ordered her to 'sit down, you are not going anywhere until I am finished.' Anger palpable from a man grieving for the loss of his first love, perhaps only love, who was his 'ballast'. Directionless, rage plunged him into desperation, making him inconsolable in grief but perhaps tormented by haunting memories. Famously known in his circles never to be interrupted, but especially at that moment as he extirpated his guilt,' his suffering must have been excruciating. There was nowhere or no one to seek consolation.

Olga Sara wrote that night, 'I am not sure what got into me, but his behaviour was outrageous. I had intended to express my thoughts after the period of mourning.' But instead, she stood up and as he approached as if to grab her by her shoulders and push her into the chair, she swung at him with her right hand and said, 'You have no authority to order me to do anything.'

Noticeably immersed by inertia, Adelia and Estrelle aghast, fell back on their chairs. 'I knew you and your children did not want me in your home from the very first day. No one paid any attention to me except Emilia and Mendes. I loved her very much too. Like my mother, she told me how much she loved me.' She taught me 'Faith is a crucial virtue. Oh my God, may she rest in peace.'

Continuing, as the attentive threesome sat upright in utter silence, Olga Sara unburdened decades of pent up animosity, making it clear that she too was inconsolable with grief. Choosing defiance, she was determined to express her anger towards him, seeking vengeance for Emilia's suffering in quiescence. On the night of the vigil for Olga Sara, her cousins told this story, dramatically animated and in greater detail.

'Uncle Dom Pedro, I know that you do not think I am a good person, but I was naïve and trusted people too easily. Trusting a priest was what I was brought up to do as I believe they must be respected and obeyed, so I trusted him. I now know better because I decided to be educated which made me ask questions to find answers. I will not ask you why you arranged for me to marry Joseph, interrupting my plans to be educated, like my cousins. I knew that you would have told me that I would have to spend the rest of my life in a convent like my mother, but what was told to me was that you used the opportunity to get me out of your home before I further damage the family's reputation.'

'You never told me you had to give Joseph a dowry, which, Emilia told me was my inheritance.' For a moment, as his daughters looked on in dismay, and they all thought he was going to explain himself. Rather, he stood up and stated firmly, 'I am leaving for Foz in the morning, on my return, I am not expecting to see any of you.' With a mournful look of retirement and exposed, like the emperor without clothes, he showed his true colours for the first time in the presence of three young ladies who were generally believed to be his daughters, only two were. Crouching like a soldier slithering away like a reptile, retreating from the battle was a man, a confabulatory, accustomed to contortions to create distortions. A confrontation that resulted in a deep fissure that was believed to make reconciliation between all of them irreconcilable.

Brazil, like other Latin American military regimes, in the early 1980s, was receiving significant global attention for human rights violations, widely and vociferously condemned at the United Nations in New York and other international agencies. Joseph believed in keeping a low profile and focussed on his work which now took him to Central American countries, the so-called 'banana republics,' for their one crop economy controlled by a handful of families, but owned and controlled by US multinational corporations.

WHO's budget for these countries' malaria campaign was shrinking as the US's focus was to train soldiers to work with its troops and providing training and supplying materiel. Officially, the US launched 'the war on drugs.' Aiming to apply maximum force to stop illicit drugs from the region, as it was also doing in Asia, from flooding the streets of the cities of Western countries. The US administrations were simultaneously devising schemes to curtail revolutionary activities to change the status quo the US was supporting. The US administration's 'War on Drugs', robbed the campaign of any chance of controlling malaria. Since the 1970s malaria has been on the rise, as has gang and gun violence. Materiel liberally handed out to Central American countries are suffusing these societies into the twenty-first century.

At home in New York, Olga Sara continued her involvement with social justice causes and devoted her time, not spent with Joseph's WHO activities or Carmelita's or Rupert's, discreetly learning more about Judaism. Fruitlessly searching for a father for half a century became an act of spiritual homage. Her relationship with Adelia and Estrelle changed significantly after Emilia's death. Visits between Miami and New York were a regular feature of their lives, but not to Sao Paulo. Bea, however, was in regular communication with her daughters.

By the mid-1980s, most of the military regimes in South America were handing over the reins of power to democratically elected governments after negotiating amnesty for military officers. In Brazil, the military also negotiated amnesty for their cronies for corruption and mismanagement. Most were associated with loans from international financial institutions. With amnesty not offered, the Faustian pact Dom Pedro had with the military did not deliver its part of the agreement. Subject to lengthy legal action, it was not surprising when his daughters informed Olga Sara that he and Bea were moving to Miami. Communication between them had ceased.

Olga Sara only discovered that Dom Pedro was ill when he sent emissaries to her. She had deliberately avoided contact since his obstreperousness at Emilia's funeral, nevertheless, she acquiesced. Death lurking beside him, Dom Pedro was regularly anointed in his South Miami mansion by priests, some visiting from Brazil. A Jesuit who was an advocate of liberation theology claimed he had an epiphany that challenged the righteousness of his arrogant belief in himself Perhaps, it came as a result of his prolonged illness which saw reconciliation with the Church and his belief in the Divine Lord.

Pugnacious from pomposity he assumed the mantle of the de Oliveira Evora empire built without fanfare over two centuries. Bedridden with clerical interrogation, the realisation came to him that he did not portray the qualities of his ancestors and more immediately his father and brothers. In his determination to achieve greatness he regularly stumbled. Counselled, he realised that he did not possess their strategic thinking and saw his youngest brother's efforts to rescue him as subversive. Clarity came in his final hour. Presumably, accepting that he could never have charted the course through the labyrinth of deception in the quest for his dynasty. They, on the other hand, had skilfully and strategically navigated a turbid course for centuries which he could not build on or maintain in over half a century. Encumbered with his self-belief of glorious hypocrisy, it ended in a maelstrom of despair. For centuries, the de Oliveira Evora descendants will be told stories about how Dom Pedro sailed into a storm of intransigence in a malaise of his own making. Uncharacteristically, but with the anointment of the last rites, he repented.

In their final meeting, Dom Pedro wanted to be alone with Olga Sara for them to pray and reflect. Expressing regret, he told her that her tirade in Sao Paulo was warranted as it accurately portrayed his demeanour. He sought rectification. Preparing for what was his last confession, he asked her forgiveness, but reconciliation was not attempted although she would have readily acquiesced for reasons which she never disclosed, even in her journal. With the last rites, he finally succumbed to acknowledging his mistakes. Realising that neither of his daughters nor Olga Sara was contemplating returning to live in Brazil, Dom Pedro had to address a matter of some urgency which he had been reluctant to do for years. And considered to be what he believed was a secret.

On his road to Damascus, Dom Pedro travelled with Father Paulo dos Santos, a Jesuit who advocated liberation theology. At five minutes past midnight, to avoid all his assets being confiscated, Dom Pedro transferred what was left in Brazil to Mendes. With this final act, he acknowledged his only son. Tragically, elephantiasis cheated Isabel from witnessing the recognition and legitimisation she sought for her son from his father. Knowing her struggles for him had been achieved would have given her enormous satisfaction, as he was finally granted entitlement to his birthright.

Reconciliation with Bea was never discussed. It was apparent that the women did not believe they should be accountable for the sins of their father and neither did his 'concubine.' Bonding with Bea and her daughters was an act of maternal intuition, realised after the death of Emilia. Also, they publicly expressed remorse for 'all the wrongs they and their father incurred.' Most importantly for them was for Olga Sara to accept a share of their inheritance, as some of it was obviously from her inheritance.'

Olga Sara, in no uncertain terms, declined. She thought that Adelia was the person 'I always knew she was,' she wrote. In Miami, Bea and her daughters established a successful property development business. Bea embraced Estrelle's conversion to Judaism. She told Olga Sara that she would teach her grandchildren, the history of the Jews and the North African Muslims or Moors who had lived in harmony in Portugal and the contribution they made to the Portuguese Empire. Unencumbered, she openly took to describing her daughters' 'noticeably Arabian eyes.'

By the late 1980s, Brazil was still struggling, adjusting to democracy after two decades of authoritarian rule. Grandmother Bea had become the de facto Emilia to Olga Sara. The two women found they had much in common and without impediments decided to contribute to society through charitable work in Sao Paulo.

Deciding to establish a charity for street children, as the economic downturn during the dying days of the military government resulted in poor and displaced families moving to the *favelas* (shanty towns) in Sao Paulo. Children were wandering the streets, not obligated to attend school, spending time seeking food and shelter and were mercilessly exploited and abused. The escalation in the number of street children in the 1990s overwhelmed the municipal authorities and church charities.

The Sarney government and the new democracy did not respond, so the police assumed responsibility to 'keep children off the streets.' Hunger drove illiterate children into gangs harassing locals. With no clear strategy to resolve the growing street crime, the police took an ad hoc approach and started moving children to provincial towns which did not achieve its objectives. With states and federal government allegedly overwhelmed, police shot and killed children to get rid of the alleged gang leaders. As the death toll mounted and poor families marched in the streets the situation gained international attention. It was not difficult for the de Oliveira women to make comparisons, thanks to Charles Dickens' novels about the 'poor houses' in London.

Tilting towards idealism, a result of the family's New York truth and reconciliation group therapy sessions, these women took it unto themselves to make a difference. A proposal from the Family Foundation to assist street children through funding education was unquestionably rejected by the government supported by military officials. The rejection seemed inexplicable to the women. After all, the family had built infrastructure in Brazil for a hundred years. Yet half a century of association with the military, allegedly for supporting authoritarian regimes and the fraudulent activities of the country's two most significant projects, had left an indelible mark on the country. The accusation was:

**'Money squandered and laundered, bribery made
commonplace and corruption unchecked.'**

Avenues of appeal were firmly shut to them and deemed useless by professional services advisors who knew the family's history. Proving that the tentacles of authoritarianism traversed the globe, creating hazards for many but opportunities for few. As a result, they were no longer welcomed into a country struggling to recover from the morass of reintroducing democracy. Without assets in the country, they would not be granted permission to visit. Not only were they barred from Brazil but threatened that it applied to all South America. The pretext was that they could be subjected to jail or abduction from which the government could not protect them. It was not certain if their names were registered with Interpol. They did not attempt to find out either.

Bea was reeling from the shock of business partners who accused them of malfeasance, resulting in all the de Oliveira

Evora becoming 'persona non grata.' Much was made of the government's amnesty. It was selective indeed. In fact, very selective. Perhaps paying for the sins of the past was to be expected. Dom Pedro's activities haunted the family. There was no prima facie case of wrongdoing. Rather, there was much publicity of the democratic government offering amnesty. What Bea and her daughters came to understand was that Brazil, and indeed other South American countries, still bear the burden of history.

As with racism, the power of the military is entrenched in institutions and society with little evidence of change. Without choice and advised against legal action and wanting to avoid public humiliation, Bea refocused on the family endeavouring to learn about Judaism as her grandson, Aaron, was preparing for his *bar mitzvah*. A coming of age Jewish ritual for a thirteen-year-old boy's transition to manhood, after a prescribed course of study with a ceremony conducted in a synagogue.

In the spirit of 'you can't keep a good woman down,' Olga Sara volunteered to assist St Joseph's church in Queens with its program of providing welfare services to teenage mothers. She believed education was the *sine qua non* of success. Olga Sara put out a call to her network of wives of Joseph's WHO team and the women in her Jewish fraternity where she had been quietly learning the Torah and about Kabbalah. The latter achieved global publicity through the pop singer Madonna and other prominent individuals in New York. The inter-religious group achieved some success and after the death of her husband Olga Sara made her faith public.

Now that it was public knowledge, Olga Sara was excited when Estrelle and her husband Stanley Hoffman invited her to participate in the ceremony. Highly anticipated, according to her journal, she told Joseph they both had to attend as Carmelita and Rupert and their families were also attending, making it the first occasion where every member of the family would be together. Not as excited as his wife, but committed to his family, Joseph explained that WHO was in the process of developing a new program. A new Foundation backed by a Seattle technology billionaire had taken an interest to provide funds with the rise of malaria in Africa and Asia.

Olga Sara spoke with Joseph on Friday confirming the details of his arrival in Miami and to inform him that Stanley and Aaron were looking forward to meeting him at the airport. When the American Airlines flight arrived, and Joseph was not on it, Stanley checked at the airline counter. Dr. Joseph dos Barros had indeed been booked on that flight but did not board the plane. He called Joseph and left a message. Then he called Olga Sara.

Frantically, she called his office several times and then her children who were arriving on Saturday. Olga Sara was reluctant to call his colleagues as she knew that most would have left the city and head for the Hamptons for the summer weekend. Rupert told his mother, 'Please do not worry, I am sure he is fine, he may have got caught up in a late meeting. I will head to his office. As everyone would have left for the weekend, I will speak to security at the night desk.' 'Please call me immediately,' his mother wistfully requested.

In anticipation and suspended animation, the household in Miami waited as children slept and Santos coffee brewed to be ready for bagels with cream cheese were in production and kept multiplying. Bea kept saying. 'It's all right.' The call Stanley took was not from Rupert, but Joseph's secretary Melinda, who lived in Manhattan and was contacted by security as they needed an employee to be present before they could enter the office.

The background noise intermingled with voices and Melinda's tears did not allow for a clear message. Stanley offered to return the call and suggested he speak with someone else who is with her. When the phone died, Olga Sara looked askance at Stanley, as hope clung to every word he uttered, which were few. In turn, everyone kept asking him to repeat what he had heard and as he was about to say for the umpteenth time. Instead, he grabbed the phone as soon he heard the first ring and without saying hello listened. In sheer frustration shouted, 'Can you please tell me what is going on?'

Aaron Hoffman's *bar mitzvah* was not the celebration his grandmother planned with her cousin Olga Sara,' as Bea still called her. She did not participate in her first Jewish coming of age ceremony. It was the talking point at the subdued celebrations as the discussion was about 'a good man committed to the cause of the eradication of the Anopheles mosquito which was responsible for over a million deaths a year'. His commitment to the cause was emblematic as it was that Friday: It saw him working when others had long taken leave. Alone, he was found lying on the floor next to a photocopying machine. Joseph's early death remained a puzzle. Speculation persisted as to whether his contact with DDT in all forms was a contributing factor to his death.

St Joseph's Church had not witnessed a requiem mass with this number of dignitaries in attendance in recent years. Officials of the WHO, UN agencies, and Latin American officials along with members of other countries' diplomatic corps filled the Church. And they all waxed lyrical, praising his contribution to world health.

Carlos de Oliveira Evora, now himself a diplomat, delivered the eulogy.

> **'Friends, Romans, countrymen, lend me your ears.**
> **I come to bury Joseph not to praise him.**
> **The evil that men do lives after them.**
> **The good is oft interred with their bones.'**

Joseph's ashes were taken to his birth place in Manaus.

Families and friends in Brazil and Argentina who did not attend the funeral in New York decided that a memorial service to celebrate his life was to be held in Manaus. A month later, another church, another city was about to have a similar but different experience in celebration of Joseph's life. A full church with standing room only heard testimony to his commitment to assisting the people of his place of birth. And especially those from the Amazon basin, where mortality from malaria continued unabated. Yet at this place, on that day, many believed that change was on the horizon. A horizon in the distance that keeps on disappearing.

Unlike the New York service of professional colleagues, the cortege at the memorial mass at the church of *Sao Sebastiao e Sao Francisco de Assis* was decidedly a family and friends' opportunity to celebrate and personalise the life of a man they respected and loved. Priests and nuns followed the procession of speakers which was opened by his younger brother Vincente. A Dominican nun, fully dressed in her habit of the Order followed, portraying elements of Carlos' eulogy. Mesmerised by a Spirit of Divine humility, looking at a questioning congregation, reciting a scripted story of a man she loved unknowingly. Olga Sara thanked her for a most unforgettable contribution to Joseph's early life. Overwhelmed from being praised, she shied away from the limelight, and in an unprecedented act was rescued into the arms of Mother Superior. Both broke conventions of the Order. But with an almighty uproar from the congregation, all were as one. In chorus. Amen.

The story Dom Pedro told Emilia when he was arranging the marriage to Joseph was of a man who lost his wife at childbirth. The accepted assumption was that mother and child died. Joseph's brother gently and quietly introduced Olga Sara to Sister Anotelia. A shy retiring woman small in stature with bright sparkling eyes and a ready smile blessed with kindness. She was brought up by her grandparents and joined the convent at twelve. Olga Sara immediately 'took to her' and from that encounter, a mother and her children would come to speak of their family of four children: two boys and two girls.

Of those who saw photographs or met Olga Sara and her children, many wanted to, but few would not dare ask. Plucking up the courage after many visits, Howard Johnson of English and Jamaican parentage and a friend of Carmelita's husband Ernesto, was the first to voice an opinion. Unexpectedly, and without notice, he arrived at the last Christmas family gathering in New York, where for the first time in many years, they were all present. Spluttering over his coffee as he waited for Ernesto, he surprised all by springing up and blurting out. 'You are a strange family you all look different and you speak differently.' He must have been disappointed if he expected a response. None was forthcoming. A mixed-race blended family had not yet entered the vernacular.

EPILOGUE

Olga Sara, drifting in a haze from a concoction of drugs, was convinced that she saw a ghost which was unlike the silhouette she saw of her mother all her life. This time, she told Carlos, 'My husband and my great uncle were sitting on either side of my bed.' They said, 'Olga Sara come with us.' When she woke from that disturbed and interrupted sleep she decided 'it was time.' Therefore, her children 'must be told the truth.'

Carlos, Carmelita, and Rupert were determined to satisfy her request. With her ashes, and in time to spread them on her birthday, they went to Portugal. Starting in Lisbon, they walked along the Tagus and headed to her great grandparents' home in Restelo. With permission from Rabbi Menachen, her ashes were taken to the Shaarei Tikva Synagogue where there was a private reading of the Jewish Memorial prayer, *El Maleh Rachamim*. Olga Sara's parents, Lia Maria and Tascha Rostowsky prayed at that Synagogue. In Evora, the soul and spirit represented by her ashes had a similar reception as at her grandparents' home, followed by a gentle stroll through the unchanged cobblestone streets and brightly painted house in the Jewish quarter. Tascha liked the area so much that he would have been happy to live there but it was not an option in 1940. Nevertheless, his professional sketches of these houses were with his family for posterity. In wanderlust, his daughter and his grandchildren confessed, 'he is a man we would have loved to know.'

Finally, their arrival in Funchal was mournfully greeted by a party of extended relatives and families who knew of Olga Sara and Lia Maria, all clad in black. Some were formerly from the orphanage and remembered her brief tearful stay. Others who were too young to remember mother and daughter spoke of the kindness of Mother Superior Francis who shone a light for her great-niece, and indeed everyone touched by her many years of service to God. In the cemetery where Olga Sara was given the amulet, all the nuns' headstones, in keeping with the tradition of the Order, bore only the date of birth and death. Recognition and memories resided with those they religiously served. To honour the only Mother Superior in the Braganza family, they knelt and prayed at her resting place, after attending a special mass at the cathedral in which all these women were honoured as 'daughters of Madeira. Olga Sara would now, like her mother, be in the island's All Soul's Day prayers. Officially, the commemoration of all the faithful departed is a typical Madeira custom. Although the second of November had passed, this occasion with much local wine, international cuisine, the music of Camille Saint Saëns, and an abundance of flowers from Palheiro was the penultimate act, before executing the final chapter in the life of The Portuguese Lady.

At dawn on 17 December 2007, the children drove to Palheiro gardens to walk their mother's spirit and soul through the roses and then, not far away, to the village of *Achada do Teixeira* from where they would hike for three hours up Mount *Pico Ruivo*, the highest point in Madeira. Lia Maria and Olga Sara intended to climb the peak. Now Olga Sara would travel on her own. Whether her mother did will never be known.

On top of the mountain in the morning calm and gentle breeze, before any visitors arrived, Carlos, Carmelita and Rupert would each recite three lines of the Celtic Blessing which they agreed to recite while spreading their mother's ashes. As Carlos started to recite his lines, the wind held its breath, allowing the sun's warmth to engulf them as they performed the recitation.

Do not stand on my grave and weep,
I am not there. I do not weep.
I am a thousand winds that blow.
I am the diamond glints in the snow.
I am the gentle autumn rain when you
awake in the morning hush.
I am the swift uplifting rush of quiet
birds in circled flights.
I am the soft stars that shine at night.
Do not stand at my grave and weep.
I am not there.

The story must end as everything in life comes to an end. As the journey of the lives of the participants have ended, but not until it has been fully told. And it can be, as the Portuguese lady wrote a reliable memoir from her heart, following the tradition of her great grandmother, which none of the men in the family ever did.

Carlos read his mother's letter, 'My children must be told I love them all dearly. Carmelita is too much like me, but I hope as she grows older will learn before it is too late, unlike me. Carlos holds a special place in my heart which you all know. Rupert, I believe knows, that Joseph was not his father. He always said he had a special affinity with his uncle Vincente. Anotela is special person. And with her, 'God Bless all my children.' Carlos did not read the 'personal letter' which was in the same envelope in his mother's hand.

Still sitting in silence as the morning drew to a close giving way to the warmth of the midday sun, Carmelita, as her mother would have done, broke the silence. 'Given your commitment to writing Mum's story, you must take these earrings.' She handed them to Carlos, eyes gushing with tears.

Carmelita told them that the night before her wedding, she was at home in Forest Hills with her parents. She and her mother discussed the common saying, *something old, something new, something borrowed, something blue.* Opening a Portuguese embroidered pouch and untying the strings, Olga Sara told her daughter to 'close your eyes and open your hands.' When she felt the cold metal in her hands, she immediately opened her eyes without permission. 'That was exactly what I did when I was seven years old and my mother put them in my hand'. Looking at those earrings, they simultaneously said, 'it is our history.'

Over two hundred and fifty years ago it was designed in the shape of the sheath of the Order of Christ, superimposed with a hand holding a bunch of flowers. On the back was *'Evora'* and the goldsmith's stamp and number. It was the first time Carmelita had seen it, so her mother explained, 'it is a family tradition to hand down those earrings to the eldest daughter on her wedding.'

Earrings from the de Oliveira Evora women handed down through generations was emblematic, testifying to the lives they lived. Staying in Portugal, they created beautifully comfortable homes, reared children, observing religious obligations, made embroidery, and with skilled Jewish artisans designed filigree jewellery. All survived in stories they told and in journals they meticulously preserved. Portuguese men left home as navigators to discover new lands and built empires to make history.

ACKNOWLEDGMENTS

A book of centuries of lifetimes, that took a decade to put together, owes much to many, especially to family and friends who for decades have been encouraging me to write this story so that they can better understand the wanderlust of the family.

To my dearest sister in Tampa who inspires me as mother did both of us, evident in how regularly we speak of her. Thanks also to the extended family scattered everywhere for their stories which inspired and compelled me to write this book.

To Virginia Hart, a friendship kindled at university and someone who is literate in good literature, and who encourages me in my writing. Quoting P.G. Wodehouse, she explained her reasoning, 'There is no surer foundation for a beautiful friendship than a mutual taste in literature.' And then there is Andrew Mason, a Yorkshire man indeed, who cannot appreciate my passion for the South Downs and New Forest for which I forgive him. His immense contribution and friendship for over two and a half decades mean more to me than he knows. And indeed, to that esteemed former journalist Steve Dabkowski, a caring friend. Thanks for checking on the book's progress which I knew was your, not so subtle hint of encouragement. Importantly, to my dear friend Eric Feinberg, with who I shared over a decade in Melbourne, but succumbed to returning home to Atlanta. Your continuing support is simply heartfelt.

To my Brazilian entourage, especially Gisa Ferreira, (mues sinceros agradecimentos querida) for her assistance on aspects of the story and especially about her former hometown, Salvador. A special mention to Livia Ce for her contribution on Salvador too, and importantly as the designer of the book's cover and the selection and advice on the maps and photographs. Obrigado. Your personal experience, history, and research make it clear why Salvador and the state of Bahia are so important in the economic and cultural history of Portugal and Brazil. Yet the contribution of the people has never been fully acknowledged by these countries and those who benefitted from it.

To Max Dumais, a confidante, and former Franciscan monk. A lateral thinker and founder of the De Bono Institute in Melbourne. who reminds me that we are a good pair as he is 'the heart and I am the head,' referring to the ethos of the Jesuits and Franciscan Orders.

To those too numerous to mention for their assistance over decades in England, Australia, the US, and Asia. To Pedro Goncalves in Lisbon, obrigado, and to the archivists for unearthing information too sensitive for the family to acknowledge and reluctant to share. Thanks for the advice to the Jesuit and Rabbinical scholars who guided my hand on these matters.

I am indebted to the work of the eminent Stanford economic historian, Professor Niall Ferguson, for his many publications on banking and finance. But more importantly for The Square and the Tower. Network, Hierarchies and the Struggle for Global Power. The meticulous research, critical analysis, and insights gave me the confidence to accept many of the stories I included in the book. This also applies to the works of Cambridge Professor Simon Sebag Montefiore, especially for Jerusalem: The Biography. Thank you.

And finally, thanks to all staff members of the stately, State Library of Victoria. Writing about centuries in a place where time stands still made immersion in history a reality.

My thanks to David Walters, the editor and team at Green Hill Publications for their assistance.

AUTHOR

Moved to Australia from England, completing a PhD at the Australian National University. Academic, Diplomat, Intelligence Analyst, United Nations peacekeeper in Cambodia, business executive, and entrepreneur. Wrote, edited, and reviewer of non-fiction books and articles in Australian and Asian newspapers and magazines. Public commentator and public intellectual. Philanthropic work in Asia.

Profits from the sale of the book will be used for the 'Street Children 'of Sao Paulo.

Lightning Source UK Ltd.
Milton Keynes UK
UKHW040729030921
389968UK00002B/316